CAMPFIRE
STORIES
of →
WESTERN CANADA

CAMPFIRE STORIES

→ *of* →

WESTERN CANADA

Barbara Smith

VICTORIA
VANCOUVER
CALGARY

To my great-grandsons,
Carson and Mason

Copyright © 2016 Barbara Smith

Heritage House Publishing Company Ltd.
heritagehouse.ca

LIBRARY AND ARCHIVES CANADA CATALOGUING IN PUBLICATION

Smith, Barbara, 1947–, author
Campfire stories of Western Canada / Barbara Smith.

Issued in print and electronic formats. ISBN 978-1-77203-112-6 (paperback)
—ISBN 978-1-77203-113-3 (epub)—ISBN 978-1-77203-114-0 (pdf)

1. Ghosts—Canada, Western. 2. Legends—Canada, Western. I. Title.

GR580.S593 2016   398.209712ʹ05   C2015-907568-8   C2015-907569-6

Edited by Karla Decker
Proofread by Kennedy Cullen
Cover and interior book design by Jacqui Thomas
Cover illustrations by Mark R / shutterstock.com

The interior of this book was produced on 100% post-consumer recycled paper, processed chlorine free and printed with vegetable-based inks.

We acknowledge the financial support of the Government of Canada through the Canada Book Fund and the Canada Council for the Arts, and the Province of British Columbia through the British Columbia Arts Council and the Book Publishing Tax Credit.

19 18 17   3 4 5

Printed in Canada

CONTENTS

INTRODUCTION

Gather 'round, happy campers. You bring the s'mores; I've brought the stories.

There are many ways to enjoy the delicious shiver of a campfire story. You could tuck yourself into your sleeping bag and scare yourself silly reading by flashlight or, even better, you can enjoy reading or telling the spooky stories around a campfire—a true staple of camping's many great joys.

If you're telling or reading a campfire story to a group, choose the story that's most suitable—to your audience and to your setting. Read the story over to yourself a few times so you're familiar with the words and the pacing—that way, when you're presenting the tale, you can concentrate on your audience.

Look up from the book frequently and make eye contact with the listeners. Think of yourself as an actor on stage performing a very short play. Change your voice tone and use gestures to help emphasize especially dramatic points.

Campfire stories usually follow a structure that includes an ending with a twist. Take advantage of that pattern by letting silence hang in the air for a moment at the end while the story settles with your listeners.

Even if you're not camping, you can still enjoy the fun of telling creepy stories. Darken the room, light a candle or two, and perhaps play some scary music.

However you choose to enjoy the stories in this book, please remember that the emphasis is on just that—enjoyment. As the storyteller, relax and enjoy the moment. You and your listeners are in for a bone-chillingly good time!

Now sit back, and don't get too scared, because the stories in this book are all just made up. Well, at least the stories that aren't true are made up—mostly made up, anyway! Besides, I've heard that restless spirits love to have their stories told. You'll see what I mean with this first mysterious adventure. It's really creepy.

ROADSIDE DINER

A couple of years ago, a few of us were heading back from a week's camping in the mountains. We'd had a great time—lots of hiking, swimming, climbing, and general unwinding. Late in the evening of our last day at the campground, we all piled into the van and headed for home. Driving at night wasn't a concern for us. We were all familiar with the route.

We were a good eighty kilometres into the trip when Gina, who was riding shotgun, noticed a strange light up ahead. We all stared at the glow, but no one could figure out what it could be.

"Maybe it's a UFO," Greg teased.

"Except it's not flying," countered his brother, Joe, who was driving.

Ashley, ever the sensible one, suggested we just keep driving till we were closer to the light and could figure out what it was.

A few minutes later, we could plainly see that the glow Gina had first spotted was a brightly lit neon sign welcoming hungry travellers to a roadside diner.

I was puzzled. "That place must be new," I said. "I've never seen it before."

"Maybe new, but totally retro," Greg noted. "Let's stop for a burger."

"I'm up for that," Joe said as he steered the van into the parking lot.

"Look at what a cool job they've done on this place," Ashley exclaimed.

"Could be right out of that old TV show *Happy Days*," Gina agreed, staring up at the sign that read RED GRILL & DINER.

Once we were inside, we saw that the attention to detail was even more impressive. Someone had gone to a great deal of trouble to re-create an absolutely accurate mid-1950s look. The floor was a checkerboard of black and white tiles. Half-a-dozen red-vinyl stools stood in front of a well-polished counter. On one side were booths upholstered in the same red vinyl, each one with room enough for all of us. We chose a booth by the window, looking out at the headlights and taillights of our fellow night-travellers zipping past on the highway. We were the only customers.

"What does everyone want?" Ashley asked.

"Well, we're here in a good old-fashioned diner, so I think we should have good old-fashioned diner food," I suggested.

A few minutes later, the door behind the counter swung open and a middle-aged woman came out. We all nearly gasped. She was done up as perfectly as the restaurant was. She was wearing a replica of an old-style waitress's uniform, including a white apron fringed with a bit of a frill and a perky little headband-hat to match. Her plastic name tag read VERA.

"What can I get for ya?" Vera asked, shifting a wad of chewing gum in her mouth and licking the business end of her pencil before pressing it against the order pad she held in her other hand. There was no doubt about it, she had her role nailed.

"I'll have fries with gravy," I said, relishing the fact that I hadn't uttered those words for a decade or more.

"Double cheeseburger for me," Joe requested.

"Make that two," his brother added.

"Cherry Coke for me," Gina said.

"Apple pie à la mode," Ashley said.

A few minutes later, Vera arrived back at our table skillfully juggling our orders.

"There ya go," she said as she unceremoniously set the plates and glasses down in front of us.

The taste of the food more than made up for what it lacked in presentation. We all nibbled from one another's plates and agreed everything was delicious.

We lingered a bit after eating, I suppose just not wanting this unique experience to end. Finally Joe stood up.

"We've gotta get on the road again," he said.

"This one's on me," I offered. "I'll go get Vera's attention so she can make up the bill."

The waitress was leaning against the counter reading a movie-star magazine.

"Ya headin' out?" she asked when she saw me walking toward her.

I nodded. "How much do we owe you?"

"Let's see—that was two double cheeseburgers, a Cherry Coke, fries with gravy, and an apple pie à la mode, right?"

I nodded again.

"Comes to $5.55," Vera said, handing me a copy of the bill.

"That can't be!"

"But it is. I know the prices are up these days, but you should've checked the menu before you ordered."

I looked at the tally. My chips and gravy cost sixty cents; double cheeseburgers were $1.75 each; the apple pie was $1.25; and the Cherry Coke twenty cents, for a total of $5.55. I handed Vera a ten-dollar bill and walked back to the van with the others.

"Must've been some kind of a special deal on there tonight," I told them. "That was a cheap round."

"We should stop there more often," Gina suggested as we drove back onto the highway.

The next week, I was telling some of my friends at work about this crazy old-fashioned diner we'd found just off the highway.

One of the fellows who had lived around here all his life looked surprised.

"Have you been there?" I asked him.

"No, I haven't, but the place you're describing sounds an awful lot like the diner where my grandparents first met. Darned shame what happened there."

"What do you mean 'what happened'?"

"Place burned to the ground. Everyone made it out safely except the waitress. My folks always said Vera gave her life for that place, and I guess in fact she did."

"Vera?"

"Yeah, she worked there, was real devoted to the place. You know, you've got me thinking. I'm pretty sure that fire happened almost exactly sixty years ago. It was around the end of August, anyway—I remember that part for sure."

THE NORTH DOOR

Mrs. Hunt breezed into the elevator of her apartment building in downtown Vancouver. For some reason, she always preferred the elevator near the north door. She pushed the button for the seventeenth floor, and as the elevator doors were sliding shut, a tall man wearing a black suit stepped through the gap at the very last second.

It was a pleasant surprise. Although there were probably two hundred people living in the high-rise, she rarely saw any of them. People tended to stay locked behind their doors, so Mrs. Hunt, who was elderly and lonely, welcomed any opportunity for a bit of socializing, even if it only lasted the duration of an elevator ride.

"Oh, you're going to the twelfth floor!" she remarked when the tall man pushed the button. "The lady with the little dog used to live on the twelfth floor, but her daughter moved her to one of those fancy retirement homes."

The man said nothing. He didn't turn to greet Mrs. Hunt with a smile or a nod, and he did nothing to acknowledge that she had spoken to him. He simply stared straight ahead, his hands clasped in front of him, his pale features fixed in a sombre expression.

A lesser woman might have been put off, but Mrs. Hunt was determined to have a conversation.

"It's nice to have a bit of company for the ride upstairs," she said. "Most of the tenants these days take the elevator by the south door, but I like this one. It's closer to my apartment."

The man did nothing and said nothing. He stared blankly ahead at the dull metallic finish of the elevator doors.

Mrs. Hunt decided to take a different approach. She would ask a direct question, which would force him to respond.

"Do you live here yourself, or are you visiting someone?" she inquired.

Still the man said nothing. Then the number twelve lit up on the bank of buttons and the elevator car shuddered to a stop. The door slid open, and the fellow with the dark suit and mood to match stepped out of the elevator onto the patterned carpet of the hall.

His departure left Mrs. Hunt with an odd feeling of disconnectedness. It made her recall a conversation she had once overheard in the lobby. One woman had been whispering to another that there was a ghost in the building, a ghost that haunted the north elevator.

Mrs. Hunt felt a little chill as she watched the silent, tall man with the vacant stare walk down the hall. As the elevator doors slid shut, she sincerely wondered if she had just met the ghost.

—

When the elevator doors closed behind him, Simon Knight felt a huge surge of relief. He decided then and there that he would only use the elevator by the building's south door from that day forward.

His neighbour had told him to avoid the north elevator, saying it was haunted. Simon had laughed at the time. He wasn't the sort to believe in such fanciful things. Of course, that was before he had ridden up those twelve floors all alone with a mysterious column of shimmering, ice-cold air.

ELIZA ANDERSON

Have you ever heard the tale of *Eliza Anderson*? The ship itself wasn't much to speak of, but the story of her final voyage will live in nautical infamy until the end of time. The battered old sidewheeler was already forty years old in 1897, when our tale begins. She'd been salvaged, not just once but twice, from the scrap heap. Those were gold-rush days, and any vessel that could be made to float, even a little, was profitably pressed into service to take prospectors up Canada's west coast to the gold veins in Alaska.

Eliza's last refitting was a quick and dirty affair. When she set out for that final long and dangerous sail, she wasn't even equipped with a compass. Author T.W. Paterson, an amateur naval historian, declared that any damage that "couldn't be patched or painted over" had been ignored. This was clearly a case of "Alaska or bust." A cynic might add that there was evidence of another unwise motto, "Safety second."

Given the pull of gold fever, it is no surprise to learn that *Eliza*'s owners saw fit to sell passage on her to two or three times as many people as the ship could safely carry, causing the mood on board to be as precarious as the ship itself.

Despite these disadvantages, *Eliza Anderson*, never a fast vessel, steamed north between Vancouver Island and the British Columbia mainland. In the waters near Comox, she collided with another ship, *Glory of the Seas*. At that point, some sailors might have had second thoughts about the wisdom of sailing without a compass, but apparently not those navigating *Eliza*. They pressed on.

As they approached the southern tip of Alaska, they sailed into a severe storm. *Eliza Anderson* was tossed about by the waves like a cork. It was all the crew could do to keep her afloat. The passengers had never been a cohesive group, and by now the life-and-death circumstances had destroyed any mutual respect they might have held.

Those circumstances were about to take a turn for the worse. The ship's supply of coal had run out. Without power, the vessel and all those in it were at the mercy of the vicious waves.

The captain did the only thing he could. He ordered the vessel stripped of every piece of flammable material. Furniture or cargo, anything anyone could get their hands on, was broken down and fed to the engine.

Even so, there was precious little hope that the ship or any on board would survive. The storm battered relentlessly at the old hulk for two days and two nights.

By the third morning, the captain had lost all track of the ship's course and position. She was out of fuel and taking on water. *Eliza Anderson* had no way of surviving, and it seemed watery graves awaited them all.

Then the captain saw a small white sailboat off to starboard. He thought he must be hallucinating. Death must be closer than he had imagined. He was so resigned to his fate that he was only mildly surprised, moments later, when he saw another impossible sight—a stranger striding across *Eliza Anderson*'s deck.

One old salt described the astonishing intruder as "a veritable giant of a man . . . with long grey hair and beard . . . looking as though he had stepped from the pages of the Old Testament." Whoever he was, this mammoth of a miracle man knew what he was about. He took the wheel and guided the boat safely through a deadly obstacle course of islets until sunrise, when the storm abated and *Eliza Anderson* came to rest in a quiet cove on the edge of a tiny island.

Passengers and crew from the failing ship fled for the safety of the island's ghost town, a long-abandoned cannery. Once the fortunate survivors regained their composure, they realized they owed a great debt of thanks to the mysterious man who had somehow boarded their ship at the height of the storm and sailed them to safety.

But that man was nowhere to be found. A few folks said they had seen him stepping into a small sailboat. Others said there was no such craft anywhere to be seen. In the end, no one knew anything for sure beyond the fact that they had all been saved from certain death.

And there the mystery stood until 1899, when a newspaper in Seattle ran an account of the event as told by "an old sailor" who claimed to have been aboard that ill-fated northbound steamer on its final voyage. He identified *Eliza Anderson*'s saviour as Captain Tom Wright, who had owned the ship when she was in her prime. This made some sense because Wright matched the physical description of the man at the wheel that dreadful night and, of course, Wright would be familiar with the vessel and capable of operating her under all conditions.

But how could Wright, an old man at the time, or anyone for that matter, have manoeuvred a small sailboat through such a storm? All that's known for certain is that something, or some-one, saved the *Eliza Anderson* and her exhausted crew from certain destruction.

LAST NIGHT

All winter long, Jake would look forward to his holidays camping beside one of the beautiful lakes in the Okanagan Valley. He loved hiking the trails, fishing, cooking over an open fire. He even loved the rainy days when he could lie in his tent reading the pile of books he hadn't had time to read the rest of the year. But of all the things he loved about camping at the lake, his favourite were his midnight swims. That first shock of the dark, cold water pouring over his skin was exquisite. Then he'd swim as hard and fast as he could from shore to the diving platform half a mile away. He would float on his back while he caught his breath and looked up at a sky full of stars. What a difference from the city!

Every year, Jake's last night at the campground was bittersweet, so he made sure he had the best midnight swim possible. One year, that last swim was decidedly more memorable than any before or since, even though it started out like any other. It was the end of August, and the water was chilly. The jolt of the cool water sent a rush of adrenaline through his body. He shivered in delight and then, as was his habit, he burst into a strong front crawl, his shoulders straining against the water. He swam hard until he reached the small dock. Fatigued but invigorated from the workout, Jake looked up. He could have sworn that the sky was an enormous black sheet pierced with pinpricks of light from the thousands upon thousands of stars high above. His shoulders slumped in relaxation. There was comfort in realizing how inconsequential a human being was compared to the mysteries of the universe.

Every other year on his last night, Jake had lingered on the diving platform to relax a little longer. This year, though, he'd taken his holidays late in August, and the warmth had drained from the air much more quickly than it did in mid-July. Soon he felt chilled to the bone and decided to swim back to shore.

Back at the beach, he grabbed his towel from the picnic bench where he'd left it and started to make his way to the campsite. He had only gone a few steps when a movement at the other end of the beach caught his attention. He wrapped the towel around his middle and stood still, straining his ears and eyes. All was dark and quiet. His mind must have been playing tricks on him.

But then, there it was again, another movement, closer this time. Light from the half moon shone brightly enough that he could make out a shape: the shape of a person. There was someone else on the beach! Jake wasn't scared, but he was surprised. In all his years of midnight swims at this spot, he had never met anyone else.

"Hello?" Jake called out in a stage whisper.

A young woman approached him. She looked as startled to see him as he was to see her.

"Hello," he said again, this time as a statement. The girl turned away from him. "Don't worry. I won't hurt you. You startled me is all. I thought I was alone."

The girl was wearing a modest red bathing suit and was shivering.

"Here, take my towel," Jake said.

When he saw her hesitate and take a step back, he smiled and added, "I have swimming trunks on underneath, don't worry."

But the girl reached to a nearby bush and picked up a towel that had apparently been hanging there. Jake was surprised he hadn't noticed the colourful towel, which was dotted with yellow circles.

"Okay then," Jake said. "At least let me walk you back to your campsite."

The two set off to the campground. A few moments later, they came to an old camper van. The lights were on inside. Jake looked to his right where the shivering girl had been standing, but she wasn't there. He scanned the horizon as best as he was able to in the dark. The girl was gone. As he stood there pondering her sudden disappearance, he noticed that an elderly man had stepped out of the driver's-side door of the van.

"May I help you?" the man asked.

Jake was too dumbfounded to speak.

The old man spoke again. "Have you come to bring our daughter home?"

Jake nodded, still speechless with confusion.

"We've been expecting you," the man continued. "We come here every year on this night, ever since the evening our daughter disappeared."

"Your daughter disappeared?" Jake managed to ask.

The man slumped in misery. "Yes, we have no idea what became of her. She may have drowned, but if she did, they never found her body. Still, every night on the anniversary of her disappearance, we come here, and every night, without fail, at some point after sunset, someone sees her—well, sees her ghost, anyway, It's the closest we can get to the daughter we loved so dearly."

Jake struggled to compose himself before answering. "I think I did see her. I talked to her. She was cold so I offered her my towel but she had her own."

"Oh, yes," the man replied. "We know all about her towel. We gave it to her. She desperately wanted a bathing suit like the one in the song. You know, 'Itsy Bitsy Teenie Weenie Yellow Polkadot Bikini,' but, of course, we wouldn't let her get such a thing. She had a perfectly fine, ladylike swimsuit. As a joke, we bought her a towel with yellow polka dots. She was such a great girl. She appreciated our concern and always told us she loved the towel and us for caring so much about her. Ironic, really. We were trying to keep her safe."

Jake steadied himself as he tried to make sense of the man's words.

"I'm sorry for your loss," Jake stammered and slowly made his way to his tent. He didn't sleep much that night. In the morning before he packed his car for the drive home, he walked to where the camper van had been parked, but there was no trace that any vehicle been there. Then he turned and headed toward the beach. Nothing seemed out of the ordinary, not until he looked over to the bushes. Was that a tuft of yellow thread snagged on a low-hanging branch? Jake reached out to pull at the tiny bit of fabric but then hesitated. Perhaps it was better just to leave well enough alone.

THE SAILORS' FATE

Karla and Declan were prairie kids, having both grown up on ranches in southern Alberta. Family holidays for each of them had always focused on the compelling landscape of the Alberta Badlands. They'd hiked the Red Deer River Valley, explored the coulees, and climbed the hoodoos. They were even familiar with the mysterious terrain of Horsethief Canyon. Neither of them, though, had ever visited Canada's west coast, so when they married, that was the destination they chose for their honeymoon.

They booked flights to Vancouver, where they rented a car and drove up the beautiful Sunshine Coast. From there, they boarded a ferry to Vancouver Island. Declan loved the sailing between the Mainland and the Island, but Karla barely saw any of the route. Her nose was stuck in a book she'd bought from the gift shop on the ferry—a book of spooky local legends. All true stories, or so the banner across the front cover proclaimed.

Once their boat had docked on the Island, the pair headed west. They could hardly wait to explore the vast beaches and endless seascapes they'd heard about.

As Declan drove, Karla read to him from the book she'd bought.

Sailors are highly superstitious folk. For instance, maritime tradition holds that renaming a boat will bring bad luck, as will sailing from port on a Friday, but neither of those cautions can hold an unlucky candle to the fear a sailor feels encountering a phantom ship—the image of a vessel that is still seen sailing the world's waterways years, even centuries, after the actual ship has sunk to her afterlife. Some phantom sightings are so vivid that witnesses have been able to read the name printed on the bow of the ship and occasionally have even heard the captain barking orders at his crew.

Karla paused and looked up from the book. "How eerie is that, Dec?" she asked.

"Well, we're not going to be out on the ocean, so I don't think there's any fear we'll see the ghost of an old ship," the young man assured his wife.

"Hah—so you say. Listen to this."

She read on.

You don't have to be on a boat to see a phantom ship. Some anomalies are visible from land. Campers and even hikers have seen these supernatural phenomena. One of the eeriest phantom ship stories comes from Canada's west coast.

Declan gave Karla a disapproving glance, so she stopped reading the book—well, she stopped reading it aloud, but she was too captivated by the strange saga to actually put the book down.

In the next paragraphs, she learned that around the middle of the last century, a sailor aboard a southbound freighter spotted a glowing ball of light on the horizon.

It was as if there was a fire burning on the water, he reported. But how could that be? Was that another ship in peril? The sailor alerted his captain, who immediately ordered their boat to change direction and head for the distressed ship.

What happened next was a story that the sailor retold many times throughout his long and adventurous life. Interestingly, those retellings never varied but went word for word like this:

> The sea was calm. The sun hadn't set. Before long we were close enough to see that, yes indeed, the glow that had been visible on the horizon was a burning ship. She was no small craft, either. She'd have needed a crew of a dozen or more to sail her. Where were those poor men? Had they already fled?
>
> We manoeuvred as near to her as we dared. Approaching any closer would've put our vessel at risk, and there didn't seem to be much point, as there was no sign of life aboard. The captain reported the incident to the authorities, who weren't surprised by our encounter. They'd had similar reports, many of them. It seems that ill-fated ship will burn into its unearthly forever.

Karla shivered. Her eyes stung with tears. She closed the book. She didn't want to annoy Declan by talking about the story, but the possibility of seeing a burning phantom ship had lodged itself into her mind. And what had happened to those poor souls who had been aboard? Could the crew have escaped, or had they been incinerated along with the vessel?

Karla gave her head a shake. She needed to push all this silliness out of her head before she ruined the trip for both of them. She drew in a deep breath and asked in the most cheerful tone she could muster:

"Should we stop for lunch soon?"

Declan smiled at her. "No need. We're almost there."

And sure enough, less than half an hour later, they pulled into a campground on the very edge of Canada. Tonight they'd be sleeping on the beach. The grandeur of the magnificent landscape pushed the spooky story out of Karla's mind.

The pair made themselves a satisfying dinner over a campfire and decided to go for a walk along the beach before calling it a day. It wasn't until they came across the burned-out ruin of a large rowboat wedged up on the beach that Karla thought again of that phantom ship and its long-lost crew.

When they got back to their campsite, Karla couldn't settle. As Declan slept, she slipped quietly out of the tent, taking a flashlight and her new book with her. She had to at least finish reading that one chapter. Cautiously, she opened the book again and read the tale's conclusion.

It wasn't until some fifty years later that the mystery of what had become of the sailors on that ancient doomed ship might have been solved.

Campers hiking along the west coast of Vancouver Island might have spotted the burned hulk's missing crew. As they looked out over the water, they saw a sight that none of them will ever forget: a large rowboat making its way slowly to shore, rowed by a crew of skeletons. It seems those sailors were doomed to forever row toward shore in a spectral lifeboat.

Karla put the book down. Could the boat that she and Declan saw that day have been that very one? Karla shivered at the thought and tucked the book into her backpack. She would wait to read the rest of the stories until they were back at home in rural Alberta, well away from the setting of this haunting tale.

ON THE ROAD AGAIN

Long before the era of personal computers and online shopping, travelling salesmen made good livings driving from place to place with the trunks of their cars chock full of everything any household might need or want—and, truth be told, many items no one really needed at all. But once a good travelling salesman managed to slip his foot in the front door, those unnecessary gadgets usually found their way into people's homes.

These mobile merchants toured the countryside, stopping at the edge of small towns before moving along to even smaller towns and finally heading out to rural areas. Whether a person lived in a big rambling farmhouse on a huge expanse of land or in a tiny bungalow on Main Street, it seemed that everyone needed, or thought they needed, at least one bottle of the latest miracle stain remover.

One such travelling salesman was a man named Dave. Dave had been at the sales game for pretty much as long as he could remember and was good at it, even if he did say so himself. Alberta was his territory, and he drove around that province from dawn till dusk, stopping at as many houses as he could. Then, toward evening, he would find a roadside motel and hunker down for a good night's sleep. His years on the road had perfected that skill, too. If there was one thing Dave did better than selling, it was sleeping. He could fall asleep in an instant, no matter where he lay his head.

One summer night, Dave steered his dusty four-door sedan into a motel parking lot. As he stopped the car, he wondered if he'd ever stayed in that particular motel before. Maybe he had, maybe he hadn't; it was hard to tell. After so many years and so many trips, he had to admit that one fleabag motel, quite frankly, looked a lot like another.

He pulled his overnight bag out of the backseat and walked to the door marked OFFICE—that is, it must have read that years ago, but by now the painted letters had faded so much that only the "o" and the "c" remained intact. Dave opened the door and stepped into a small, dark room. A woman stood beside a well-worn linoleum counter. For someone in the hospitality business, she wasn't very welcoming. She didn't even bother saying hello but just stared at Dave until he finally said, "I'd like a room for the night."

"Pretty much full up here tonight," the woman told him in a low, rumbling voice.

Dave glanced back at the parking lot. His was the only car.

The woman coughed before speaking again. "I'll let you have my last room. Don't usually rent that one out, but I'll do you a favour."

She set an oversized key on the counter and said, "Bring this back before nine tomorrow morning."

Dave nodded. He was just too tired to discuss details. He needed a hot shower and a good night's sleep. The number on the key was 13. *Good thing I'm not superstitious*, he thought.

The door to room 13 opened easily. Dave dropped his suitcase and ran his hand along the wall searching for a light switch. Seconds later, a single bulb hanging from the ceiling rewarded him with a pale puddle of light. Across the room, he could see a small bed with a metal frame.

Charming, he thought sarcastically as he kicked off his shoes and loosened his tie. *Guess it'll have to do.*

He sat down on the bed. The metal slats beneath the thin, lumpy mattress squeaked in protest.

Don't know how many more trips like this I have in me, he reflected as he leaned back against the bars of the bed's headboard. He closed his eyes and was already drifting off to sleep when something startled him. He sat bolt upright. What was it? A noise? Dave looked around the room. Did something move over there by the door? Yes, something had moved. A rat? No, nothing moved. It was nothing. Besides, there weren't supposed to be any rats in Alberta.

So tired, I'm seeing things, he thought, reaching into his suitcase for his pajamas. *Tomorrow morning there would be plenty of time for a shower.*

Despite the uncomfortable bed, Dave fell asleep quickly. Trouble was, he didn't stay asleep very long. Something disturbed him. A sound? A movement? He sat up in bed, his eyes drawn to that same dark corner. There was something there. Something vague, soft-looking. It was pulsing, vibrating. Suddenly the room was freezing cold. Dave clutched at the thin blankets. He pressed his back up against the unforgiving metal bars, staring in horrified disbelief as the movement expanded and grew taller, into a column of dim shimmering light.

A foul smell oozed into the room. Dave's hand flew to his face in a vain attempt to block the awful odour. His breath was coming in short, quick gasps. *Please let me be dreaming,* he pleaded inwardly. Because if he wasn't dreaming, then he was watching a vibrating pillar of light form before his eyes.

Slowly the vaporous column solidified—into a human form! Dave couldn't make out the face, but there was no denying this was an apparition of a man wearing a plaid shirt and overalls. The man stared at Dave curiously. There was no hostility in his ghostly eyes, but even so, this was a frightening sight.

The two souls—corporeal and ethereal—held one another's gaze until finally the manifestation began to dissolve into sparkles of light before dispersing as silently as it had formed.

Dave drew in a breath. He should have taken that pension when his boss offered it to him last month. That way he could have finished his career without ever having seen a ghost. Rundown motels were one thing, but a haunted, rundown motel was entirely more than he had ever bargained for, and it ruined his record of always sleeping well through the night. The next morning he couldn't wait to check out. As he handed the woman behind the counter his credit card and the oversized room key, a photograph on a nearby shelf caught his eye. It was a picture of a man wearing a plaid shirt and overalls.

"Who's that?" he stammered.

"Oh, that's Wilf, my husband. My late husband, I should say. Nice enough guy, I guess, but between you and me, my life's simpler without him. He was the nosiest man ever to draw a breath—eternally showing up in places where he didn't belong."

THE HOOK

At a certain private campground on Vancouver Island, a dance was held every Saturday night in an enormous tent. All the campers were invited, and that is how one particular young couple met. After a few slow dances together and some conversation, the young man was hopeful that romance might be in the air. He suggested that they go for a drive in his car. The girl agreed, but she soon felt they had driven too far. By the time she spoke out, they were on a dark, deserted stretch of road.

"It's getting late. I don't think this is a good idea," she declared.

"I'll stop if you like," he assured her. "We can do a little stargazing and get to know each other better."

He steered the car to the side of the road and turned off the ignition. They were deep in the forest. Towering coniferous trees surrounded them. Only the merest sliver of the moon, but no stars, shone through the forest.

"We can't see the sky from here," the girl pointed out, but the young man didn't reply. He seemed content just to look at her. He slid across the front seat and put his arm around the girl.

She allowed him to kiss her, but she was wary and kept her eyes wide open. The young man could sense her discomfort and eventually couldn't hide his frustration any longer.

"Don't you like me anymore?" he asked with an edge to his voice.

"I'm frightened out here in the middle of nowhere. My friend told me there's a deranged killer on the loose."

The young man had heard that story, too, but he was sure that that was all it was, just a story: gossip, rumour. People called the killer Captain Hook because he had a metal hook where his right hand had been.

"That's a bunch of malarkey," he assured the girl. "There's absolutely nothing to worry about. Besides, I'm here to protect you."

With that, the young man advanced upon the girl again, wrapping her tightly in his arms. For a few minutes, she tried to get into the spirit of things, but every snap of a twig or moan of the wind in the trees made her jump and shiver with fear.

When she gasped, "What's that?" the young man ran out of patience.

"It's nothing!" he snarled. "There's no one else here. When will you stop behaving like a scared little kid?"

His taunt sent the girl into a fit of tears.

"I am scared," she sobbed. "I can't shake this horrible feeling that something bad is about to happen."

"Something bad *has* already happened," the young man seethed. "You've ruined our evening. We might as well just drive back."

He started the car, slammed the transmission into gear, cranked the steering wheel around, and stepped on the gas pedal. The tires spun for a second then gripped, sending out a spray of dirt and gravel. The car bounced and swerved violently before he regained control.

Inside the car, neither he nor she said a word. The young man drove aggressively, demonstrating his fury over being rebuffed in such a childish way. She sat as far away from him as possible. Her shoulders sagged with relief when she saw the lights of the campground up ahead. Now she felt foolish for having been so nervous.

The young man stopped the car by the oversized tent where the dance party was still going strong. He decided to act like a perfect gentleman just in case anyone was watching. He got out of the car and started to walk around to open the passenger's side door for the girl. As she watched him, the girl felt even more foolish, thinking that she'd misjudged him. She decided to just sit where she was until he opened the door for her.

But he had disappeared. Where was he? Had he gone into the dance tent and just left her in the car? She looked out her side window. The young man was there, standing several feet away, looking pale and shaken, his face twisted into an expression of revulsion and horror. His gaze was fixed upon the passenger's door of the car.

"What's wrong? What is it?" the girl cried, opening the door and jumping out of the car.

Her movement jolted the young man out of his trance.

"Don't look," he begged her. "Don't look!"

But the girl couldn't stop herself. She turned in the direction of the young man's gaze and fell to the ground in a dead faint.

There, hanging from the handle of the passenger-side door, was a gleaming metal hook.

ETERNALLY CARING

On a pleasant spring afternoon in 1950, the Sinclair family was enjoying a short holiday in Calgary, Alberta. The parents were sitting on a bench by the river while their young sons, Jamie and Ricky, played nearby. Mr. Sinclair had just told his wife that black-and-white televisions might soon be replaced by full-colour screens. Mrs. Sinclair sighed and said she was sure the younger generation, her own two sons included, would be ruined by the phenomenon. For now, though, the boys were happily by the lake feeding the geese bits of bread they had left over from the sandwiches they'd eaten for lunch.

After a time, a young woman wearing a long, blue cloak walked toward the boys. She had a handful of broken biscuits that she was throwing, one by one, toward the birds. Since the children had used up all of their bread crusts, they turned their attention to the stranger.

"Lovely day," said the woman.

The two needed no further encouragement. They launched into a long line of chatter about the swans and the weather and the vacation house on Kensington Road where they were staying for a week with their parents. The woman asked them where they were from, and did they attend school there, and did they have any other brothers or sisters. The boys eagerly answered each query.

The woman smiled wistfully and said, "I so enjoy the company of children—much more than that of adults, I must say. Perhaps it's because I worked for so long in the children's ward at the hospital here."

"Don't you work there anymore?" Ricky asked.

The woman didn't answer. She did not even appear to have heard the boy's question. She was focusing intently on something in the distance.

"Be careful!" she shrieked suddenly. "Be careful—you could fall in and drown!"

Ricky turned around, following the woman's frightened gaze. He spotted Jamie at the edge of the river, starting to climb up on the remnants of an old bridge. His brother looked sheepish and confused. He had no idea what he had done wrong, and the boys were not used to being chastised by strangers.

"I only wanted to look down into the river. It's not deep," he explained.

"But it's very dangerous," she insisted sternly.

Jamie and Ricky looked at each other uneasily. They were relieved a moment later to hear their father calling them back to the bench.

"Nice to meet you," they mumbled politely as they turned to join their parents. The young woman did not appear to hear them as she stood wringing her hands fretfully.

Jamie was worried that he might receive a second dressing-down from his parents, so he began laying out his defence before they could say a word.

"I was being careful by the water," he said. "You know I'm always careful. That woman was nice to talk to, but, if you ask me, she was a bit nervous."

Ricky nodded in agreement, but Mr. and Mrs. Sinclair only looked at each other with confused expressions.

"What woman?" they said in unison.

Now it was the children's turn to appear confused.

"That lady in the long blue cloak," Ricky said. "She was right there with us for the longest time. You must've seen her."

Mr. and Mrs. Sinclair insisted that they had not seen anyone. *Such imaginations*, they thought as they gazed at their children, while the boys wondered how they could possibly have *not* seen her. But no more was made of the matter.

That afternoon, Jamie was stung by a bee. The bite swelled so badly that Mrs. Sinclair insisted they take him to the hospital. Once they were there, the parents sat in the waiting room with Ricky while a friendly young nurse from the children's ward tended to Jamie. It wasn't long before the boy was feeling much better and was once again his chatty, curious self.

"We met another nice young woman this morning," Jamie said. "She said she used to work here at the hospital."

"It must've been some time ago," the nurse replied. "We haven't had any staff changes for several years."

Jamie looked doubtful. "Couldn't have been too long ago. She looked young, like you."

The nurse stared at the boy. "Wait just a moment. I have to get something."

When she came back, she was carrying a faded photograph. She showed it to Jamie, whose face lit up with recognition.

"That's her!" he said brightly. "That's the nurse we met."

"I thought it might be," the nurse said quietly before sending the lad back to join the rest of his family.

Mr. Sinclair was the first to notice the nurse coming down the hall toward the waiting room. He saw how pale she looked and noted that the friendly smile had left her eyes.

"Nothing's wrong, I hope?" he asked her anxiously when she entered the waiting room.

"Wrong? No, no, not at all. Jamie's fine. Ready to go, in fact. If my manner startled you, I'm sorry, but I've just had a bit of a shock."

She then pulled the creased photograph from the pocket of her uniform and showed it to Mr. and Mrs. Sinclair.

"I realize that this is an odd question," she began, "but have you ever seen this woman?"

Mr. Sinclair shook his head.

"No, never," Mrs. Sinclair said.

"I have!" said Ricky. He had come up behind his parents and was peering at the photo. "That's the woman we met this morning when we were feeding the swans!"

"I saw no one with you," Mr. Sinclair said firmly, tired of hearing about some woman neither he nor his wife had seen.

"But she was there," Ricky protested.

Before his parents could say another word, the nurse spoke again.

"You may both be right," she said. "This is a photo of my friend, my best friend. Jamie also identified her as the woman they were talking to this morning."

"Yes, she was very nice," Jamie said. "Easily upset, though. She got herself quite worked up when I climbed up on the bridge."

"Well, now," the nurse said thoughtfully, "that makes sense."

"It makes *no* sense," Mr. Sinclair blustered. "This is ridiculous. We were right there with our sons this morning."

The nurse turned to the boys and asked them to sit in the waiting room. Then she led the parents around the corner into the hall. There, in whispers, she explained herself.

"I think it's possible that your sons met my friend today," she said, "and I think it's equally possible that you did not notice her presence. You see, my friend . . . " She paused for a moment and looked behind her to make sure that the children were well out of earshot. "My friend was always very fond of children. Very concerned for their safety."

"Be that as it may . . . " began Mr. Sinclair.

"She died four years ago," the nurse continued.

The Sinclairs stared at her in shock.

"I believed your children when they identified her in the picture, but what convinced me thoroughly was Jamie describing her agitation when he was near the water."

"Why was that?" asked Mrs. Sinclair in a voice as dry as sand.

"Because of how she died," the nurse replied. "My friend was trying to save a little boy who'd fallen into the river, but she slipped and fell headfirst against a rock. She died instantly."

"How terrible," muttered Mr. Sinclair.

"Yes," the nurse agreed. "It was very tragic." Then, almost as an afterthought, she added something more.

"It was only by chance she was even there at the bridge that day. It was only because she had a few broken biscuits that she wanted to feed the swans."

A TRUE GENTLEMAN

Natalie was not an outdoorsy sort. She was, however, a good sport, so she joined a group of friends camping just east of Banff. But by the third day at the campsite, Natalie needed a break. She needed to see civilization again, even if it was just for a few hours. After assuring her friends that she'd be back by bedtime, Natalie got into her car and drove toward the outskirts of Calgary. What a relief! Proper roads, not hiking trails, and lots of buildings instead of tree-covered mountains, definitely a sight for her urbanite sore eyes. Who would have thought that concrete could be so reassuring? Better still, she could see that there was a shopping mall just ahead. She steered her car into the parkade and hurried into the nearest store. This was exactly what she needed—a little retail therapy.

Hours later, when the stores were closing, Natalie realized she had stayed in the mall far longer than she intended to. Her friends would be concerned about her. Lugging her parcels, she hurried to the parkade. The place didn't look anything like it had when she'd first pulled her car into a parking space several hours earlier. Now it was dark and empty. Her footsteps echoed ominously. Worse, she couldn't remember where she had parked. Her breath was coming in short, sharp gasps. She could hear her pulse thundering in her ears.

Should she go up to the next level? She would have to, because her car certainly wasn't on the first level. The stairs between the levels were horrible: dirty, dark, and shadowy. A whimper escaped her lips. She was sorry she'd left her friends in their beautiful, tranquil campground. Just as she was wondering if she'd ever see the mountains again, Natalie stepped from the stairwell to the second floor of the parkade, and there was her car! Tears of relief ran down her cheeks. She promised herself she would never lose track of time again.

Feeling much braver, she pulled out her keys and walked around to the driver's side of the car. Then her heart sank lower than she would have thought possible. The rear tire was flat.

Not willing to make the trek down those awful stairs and across that huge parking lot back to the shopping mall, Natalie decided to do the only thing she could do in the circumstances. She opened the trunk of her car and pulled out the jack. She would change the flat tire herself.

Fifteen frustrating minutes later, she regretted her decision. She wasn't strong enough to loosen the lug nuts on the wheel, and the time she had spent working on them meant there was no hope anyone would be left in the shopping centre. She slammed her hand down against the car in frustration.

"May I help you?"

Natalie gasped and swung around. A man stood behind her. The noise she'd made angrily hitting the car must have covered up the sound of his footsteps. Neatly dressed in a suit and carrying a leather briefcase, he didn't look dangerous.

Must be a businessman, she thought before answering the man's offer.

"I do need some help," she said and explained that she'd tried to change the tire herself but hadn't been able to.

The man dropped his expensive-looking briefcase into the open trunk of Natalie's car and set to work. Mere moments later, the spare tire was on the rim and the flat one in the trunk. The man closed the trunk lid with an exaggerated flourish and offered a mock bow.

"May I give you some money for your trouble?" she offered.

"No, not at all," he assured her. "I'm running a bit late now, though. I wonder if you could drive me to my car. It's on the next level of the parkade."

Natalie stiffened. She didn't like the idea of letting a complete stranger into the car with her, but he *had* done her a great favour. She supposed she should at least be polite enough to give the man a drive to his car. Natalie took a closer look at the man. He really did look harmless. She sighed and walked around to unlock the passenger's-side door of the car. And that's when she noticed. The man might be wearing a business suit, but he was also wearing sneakers. That's why she hadn't heard him coming up behind her. It wasn't that the noise she'd made banging her hand against the car had covered up the sound of his footsteps. His rubber-soled shoes wouldn't have made any noise.

What man wears running shoes with a suit?

The answer hit Natalie like the smack she'd given the car. *A man who wants to sneak up on someone.* She turned on her heel and ran as fast as she could back to the shopping mall. Luck was with her. A security guard was just checking the set of doors she was running to. Out of breath, the terrified young woman explained what had just happened. Hearing herself describe the encounter, she thought she sounded silly, like a scaredy-cat—worse, a rude scaredy-cat who wouldn't even give a gentleman a drive to his car.

"I probably panicked for nothing," she told the guard. "I'm sorry. It's just that my friends are waiting for me at the campground and I shouldn't even have come into the city and . . . "

"Don't you worry," the guard assured her. "That's why we're here. I'll be glad to walk you to your car."

There was no sign of the man anywhere in the parkade. Relieved, Natalie unlocked the driver's-side door. That's when she remembered! The helpful man's briefcase was in the trunk of her car. How could she have been so rude? Now it seemed she really had inconvenienced the person who had helped her.

"I feel dreadful about this," she told the guard.

"Never mind, there'll be identification in his briefcase. We can get it back to him tomorrow morning."

Natalie opened the trunk lid. The guard lifted out the briefcase and pulled it open. There wasn't any identification inside. Instead, there was a coil of rope and a hunting knife.

This had been no gentleman, Natalie realized. Her voice shook as she asked, "Does he wander around parkades at night looking for someone whose car has broken down?"

"Probably not," the guard said quietly as he pointed to a third object in the briefcase. It was an awl, a piercing awl, one with just enough heft to puncture a car's tire.

THE CAPTAIN'S WIFE

A particular ship's captain was known as a nasty piece of work. It's been recorded that this man was "hard on his sailors" and "a dried-up old fossil who lived like a recluse ashore and never left the bridge of his ship while at sea."

An even more disturbing oddity about the man was that he would periodically go into something of a trance and insist that he could hear the bell of a ship that had gone down off the Pacific Coast many years before. Usually he would snap out of his foggy mental state, and when he did, he'd always tell his crew that he was determined to find that sunken ship.

One day, however, the sailors were suspicious that their leader had stayed in one of his trances because he ordered a sailor to gear up, dive down to the bottom, and bring back the submerged vessel's name board.

Knowing that refusing an order could bring a charge of mutiny, the sailor climbed into the deep-diving apparatus and dove below. Oddly, once he was under the water he, too, could hear the ringing of a submerged ship's bell. He went down deeper. Sure enough, there was a wreck lying on the seabed.

The diver was nearly out of air when he finally spotted the ship's seaweed-covered, disintegrating name board. He ripped the piece of wood free and rose to the surface as fast as he dared.

Once he was back on board, the diver handed his find to the captain, who became nearly delirious with excitement and insisted that he himself go down to the ocean floor and see the wreck for himself.

Knowing that the captain wasn't qualified to use the sophisticated diving equipment, the crew tried to get him to change his mind, but he was determined. He went down to the hold and dug out an old-style diver's suit. He insisted that his men help him into the heavy, awkward gear. Then, amid their protests, the captain lowered himself over the side of the ship. He sank below the waves instantly, leaving only the air hose and lifeline visible.

A few minutes later the crew was shocked to see the end of the air hose float to the surface beside their vessel. They knew immediately that something dreadful had happened. They tugged on the lifeline in hopes of pulling the captain back to the surface, but the line offered no resistance. Fathoms below, the captain had cut through both his lifesaving tethers. He had chosen to die among the bones of the sunken ship.

The sailors had no option but to return to port and share their tragic tale with the authorities. Interestingly, a naval record keeper had some information to share with them. That long-lost wreck was the very same ship the captain's wife had been aboard decades earlier, when the ship had vanished beneath the waves, taking with it all its passengers.

THE LATE MR. FORMAN

"I've had an encounter with a ghost, you know," Uncle John said as he poked a twig at the campfire.

Larry and Rob exchanged glances. They had learned over the years that their uncle was a tireless kidder, so they sat quietly in the deepening dusk waiting for his punchline. But he didn't speak again for quite a while. The only sounds were the fire's crackle and the occasional hoot of an owl high in a nearby tree.

Finally John continued, "I suppose I might as well tell you the whole story. Of course, this happened years ago, but still it happened, and not all that far from where we're camping right now."

Larry pierced two marshmallows through a scorched stick and extended the snack-in-waiting over the fire's glowing embers. His hand shook a bit. He pulled his other hand from the pocket of his hoodie and rubbed his jaw. There was something disquieting in their uncle's tone and it had set Larry's nerves on edge—well, that and being alone at night in the woods with only a nylon tent and an unreliable pickup truck between them and the wilderness.

John took a sip of the hot, sweet tea he had brewed over the campfire and then cleared his throat before speaking again.

"I still remember every detail. That's how unsettling it was."

Both boys turned to look at their uncle, who seemed to be staring off into a space. Tension hung in the air as they waited to hear his story.

"I was out of town on business quite a bit that year. During the week leading up to Halloween, I was here on Vancouver Island, in Victoria. I was busy with work during the days, but the evenings were long and boring. I didn't know anyone in town. The front-desk clerk at the hotel suggested that I might get a kick out of the guided ghost walk in the nearby cemetery. I'd never heard of such a thing, so I was curious."

Larry started to snicker. "I've been on one of those, at home, in Edmonton. The thing was so cheesy, it was pathetic. I could tell it was going to be hokey right from the beginning."

"Well, I missed the beginning of this one," John continued, "so I don't know about that part, but this guy did a great job telling all the stories."

"We heard that about you, Uncle John, that you were always late," Rob teased.

"That's true," John nodded. "In those days I was never on time for anything, but that was about to change. Just after I caught up with the group, another man turned up and stood right beside the guide. I figured he was with the tour company and that he would be telling some stories, but he didn't say a word. He just tagged along. Toward the end of the tour, people were chatting with the storyteller and asking him questions. I had a couple of questions myself. I hung back a bit at first, but it looked as though he was going to be busy with those other folks for quite a while, and frankly, I was getting cold."

Larry poked at the fire and a log slipped farther into the flames. Rob jumped at the sudden noise. Both young men had obviously been paying rapt attention to their uncle's recounting.

John continued. "Still, though, I did have a question I wanted to ask, and I figured the second guy must be a guide in training so I walked over to him. I remember thinking that he wasn't dressed warmly enough for the weather, no jacket or anything. I asked him if he was with the tour company and then added that I thought the tour was very well done. He didn't seem to hear me. Just then the actual guide announced that the tour was over and we should start walking back to the street."

Larry shrugged his shoulders in Rob's direction. There hadn't been much point to their uncle's story.

Then John spoke again. "The guy I tried to talk to had something in his hand, like a big coin. He set the thing on top of a gravestone. I glanced down for a second to see what it was he'd put there, but it was too dark to make it out. Then I looked up again. I was going to remind him to take whatever it was with him, but he wasn't there anymore. The man had simply vanished. He was there one second, as solid as you or me, and the next, he was gone."

"Don't you think he might just have ducked down behind another grave marker?" Rob asked hopefully.

"No," John said emphatically. "It wasn't like that at all. He was there, and then he wasn't."

"So you think he was a ghost?" Larry asked.

"It's not that I think he was a ghost. I know he was a ghost and I'll tell you why I know this. The next morning I checked out of the hotel room early and went back into the cemetery. I remembered where we'd been the night before, and I went directly to that grave. There, on top of the slab of marble, was a watch—an old-fashioned pocket watch. I picked it up. It was icy cold."

Rob chuckled. "Well, of course the watch was cold. It had been outside overnight."

"Maybe so, but it seemed even colder than it should've been. I could barely touch it at first. I did see that the back cover of the watch was engraved with the initials WGF. I looked at the gravestone. The name on it was Winston Graham Forman."

Both Larry and Rob drew in deep breaths. "What did you do?" Joe asked quietly.

"Well, I phoned the company that ran the ghost tours and told them that one of their assistant guides had left a keepsake behind in the cemetery. They insisted that there was only ever one guide on any of their tours. I explained about the guy joining late, but they insisted that didn't happen."

"Well then, Uncle John, maybe it didn't. I wonder if you were tired and imagined the whole thing."

"I'd wondered about that, too," John said as he reached into the front pocket of his windbreaker and pulled out a shiny silver disk. "I've carried Winston Graham Forman's watch with me every day of my life since his ghost left it for me that night in Victoria on the cemetery tour."

"The watch is still working?" Rob asked.

"Well, that depends on how you define 'working.' This beautiful old piece doesn't keep time anymore, it's true, but carrying a ghost's watch certainly does something to remind a person of the importance of being punctual."

FAMILY TIME

Gary and Carol had both enjoyed their careers as high school teachers in a small town east of Red Deer, Alberta, but even so, the day they retired was one of the happiest days in their lives. The very next morning they packed their camper van and hit the road. They were looking to buy their retirement home.

They'd had more than their share of prairie winters, so they planned to move to the Interior of British Columbia. They didn't need a big house, but they did want lots of land so their children and grandchildren could come to visit and camp out on the property.

As the couple drove, they sang along to tunes on the radio and chatted about the future, occasionally peeking in the rear-view mirror to watch Alberta's beautiful big blue sky recede behind them. Late that afternoon, they stopped at a campground near Golden, BC, and early the next morning they headed out again. Soon they were off the main highway and exploring country roads. Gary drove slowly while Carol watched for real estate signs. There weren't many.

"This is such a beautiful area," Gary said. "People must hang on to any property they have here."

Then, as they rounded a bend in the road, Carol thought she spotted something.

"Gary, stop the car. I think I saw a sign," she said. "Just back up a bit. You see? Right there—it looks as though there used to be a driveway."

Gary peered through the windshield.

"Is that the sign you saw?" he asked as he laughed and pointed to a weather-beaten, hand-painted piece of board nailed to a tree. "I don't think that's what a real estate agent would call a 'current listing.' I doubt there's even a house there any longer."

"Well, let's drive in a bit anyway. If there's a clearing in the woods, we can sit and eat our picnic lunch."

Gary nodded and drove farther along the overgrown track.

"Keep going," Carol encouraged as the car inched forward, bramble bushes scratching the hood and windows.

It was obvious that no one had driven on the path for many years.

Then, as Gary manoeuvred the car up a slight rise, the brush thinned, and there, right in front of them, was an old dilapidated house. Another hand-painted sign trailed at an angle from the remains of the clapboard frame. No doubt at one time that sign had also read FOR SALE.

"Oh Gary, can you believe it? We might have found our house!"

"You can't be serious. This place is falling down."

"Where's your love of a challenge? We could fix it up. We should at least take a look at it. Let's go in."

Carol was out of the car and striding toward the rickety stairs leading from the even more rickety verandah before Gary had turned off the ignition.

"Carol, stop," he called. "This isn't safe. As it is, we're trespassing, for goodness' sake."

He climbed out of the car muttering under his breath, knowing full well that his wife wasn't listening. She was already walking through the front door, or rather at a spot where the front door used to be. By now only a few pieces of wood hung from one remaining rusty hinge. Annoyed, but also worried about his wife's safety, Gary hurried to join to her.

The nauseating odour of decay permeated the dark interior. Despite her best efforts to appear confident, Carol choked and gagged.

"You're right. This place is bad," she said.

Gary tried to offer a teasing "told you so," but his solar plexus had tightened, choking off his words. The place looked like an overdone setting from a horror show. The air was so thick with dust that they could only see the barest outlines of old furnishings, and those were decorated with lacy cobwebs.

Gary rubbed his eyes. A table, set for a long-ago meal, and chairs stood in the middle of the room. In the kitchen just beyond, plates held mouldy food that had crumbled to dust.

As they stood gazing at this extraordinary sight, Gary's annoyance and Carol's curiosity changed to awed humility. They were witnessing remnants of lives once lived. As they stared through the dust motes at the sepia-toned vision, an icicle of horror slithered down Gary's spine. Carol gasped. There, staring back at them, were forms: a man, a woman, and two small children. Their images were still, flat, and two-dimensional, their eyes dull and lifeless.

Carol tugged at Gary's hand and the two fled from the house, across the yard, and into the safety of their car. Only then did they breathe again, letting the extraordinary reality of what they had witnessed settle into their minds and hearts. The manifestations they had seen were not corporeal beings. Those were ghostly remnants from long ago.

Gary fumbled with the car key until his shaking hand found the ignition. Neither of them spoke as Gary backed down the abandoned driveway and onto the country road.

They drove in silence until they came to a crossroad. There, not far away, was a gas station. Neither of them spoke until they were stopped at the side of the building.

"You okay?" Carol asked her husband.

He nodded. "You saw them too, didn't you?"

This time it was Carol's turn to nod. Minutes passed as each mulled over the supernatural scene they had witnessed. They were so distracted with their thoughts that they didn't notice a man from the service station approaching their car.

"Hey folks! How ya doin'?"

The couple jumped and stammered as best they could that they were fine.

Gary recovered his composure first. "We just stopped to see if you had any cold drinks for sale. We're both pretty thirsty."

He got out of the car and walked with the attendant to a pop machine at the front of the building. He bought a drink for himself and one for Carol. He knew she'd welcome the refreshment.

"Out for a Sunday drive?" the man inquired.

Gary nodded. "We're looking for some property to buy."

"Nothing much for sale around here," the man said, shaking his head. "Well, except the old Fletcher homestead along that crossroad a bit, but that place has a bad reputation."

"Really?" Gary held his cold bottle of pop against his face.

"Terrible thing. Happened decades ago, 'bout the middle of the last century, if my sources are correct. A neighbour found them. All four of them—father, mother, and both kids. Dead. Cops finally determined they'd been poisoned, all of them. To this day, no one knows if it was an accident or murder."

When Gary didn't reply, the man asked, "You okay, buddy? You don't look so good. You've gone pretty pale."

"I'll be fine," Gary stammered. "Thanks for the information. Better get back to the car. My wife'll be looking for her drink."

The couple drove away, drinking their sodas in silence and trying to wash away the reality of their unreal encounter.

The service station owner walked back to the building, shaking his head.

"Seems like the haunting at the old Fletcher place's still active, Gert," he said to his wife.

The woman nodded. "Wonder how much more spirit those poor souls have in them."

The next day, Gary and Carol found their dream home, a small place in great shape surrounded by lots of partially cleared land. Their children, and eventually their grandchildren, camped there often. Every summer evening, when the family gathered around the dinner table, Gary and Carol would exchange glances, remembering the images of those souls haunting that ramshackle house.

THEATRE OF LIFE

Nothing's more fun than camping in the Okanagan, unless rain has been pouring down for two days with no end in sight and you're alone in a leaky tent waiting for your friends to join you. Then it's no fun at all, and your only choice, short of packing up and going home, is to drive into the nearest town and see a movie. You might want to be careful which town and what theatre you choose.

Jim had longer summer holidays than his friends did, so they decided that he should drive out to the campground a few days ahead of the others and hold the spot for them. But by the morning of the third day at the campground, Jim just couldn't take it anymore. He was thoroughly miserable. He couldn't decide which was worse, the brain-numbing boredom or the discomfort of being constantly damp and chilly. What he knew for certain was that he was at the end of his patience and badly needed a break from the miserable isolation. He did the only thing he could think of: he got into the car and drove along the muddy campground road out to the highway and into town.

Of course, it was raining there, too, and the main street was deserted. *So much for reaching out to my fellow human beings,* he thought as he parked the car by a drugstore and scanned the street looking for a movie theatre. *There had to be one, and maybe that's where the townsfolk were,* he thought. *They've all gone to the movies because they're sick of the deluge, too.*

Jim's optimism slipped when he couldn't see any theatre at all, let alone a crowded one. But surely every little town had a cinema. He didn't even care what film they were showing. He'd take an old western or even a romcom if he had to. His shoulders slumped as he sat in his car watching the rain bounce on the hood. Clearly, he was going to have to haul his sorry self out from the protection of the car and take a walk along Main Street.

The downpour blurred what he could see of his surroundings, giving the town a surreal, dreamlike look—well, not so much a dream as a nightmare, really. This place was just plain creepy: a deserted ghost town. A cold, fat raindrop trickled under Jim's shirt collar, making him shudder.

He'd had enough, more than enough. Being the placeholder for his friends' camping spot had entirely lost its appeal. He turned back toward his car.

But wait, was that a kid leaning against the passenger's door? It was. Where had he come from?

"Hey, kid!" Jim yelled. "Don't go scratching my car."

The child looked up but didn't move.

Jim hurried his pace.

"Hey yourself," the child echoed in a whisper, as if actually speaking was more effort than he was able to give.

Jim's shoulders tensed. He stopped, looked at the boy again, and sighed. He knew that cabin fever could wind a person up, but he had to have enough maturity and sense left not to want to deck a ten-year-old kid. He drew in a deep breath before he spoke.

"Guess you're standing by my car 'cause it's the only one here, right?"

The boy held his gaze.

"Everyone but you staying home today 'cause of the rain?"

This time the child offered a slight nod.

"Okay, so I'm rained out of my camping spot. Is there a movie theatre here in town?"

The boy lifted his arm and pointed behind Jim.

Sure enough, there it was. No wonder Jim hadn't seen it before. He hadn't been looking for a Quonset hut: a Quonset hut with a marquee—of sorts.

"Thanks," Jim said hesitantly. Should he ask the kid if he wants to go to the show with him? That would get him away from the car, at least. Nah, that would be too creepy, and he's not really doing anything to the car anyway. Jim waved and walked toward the theatre door.

The lettering on the door proclaimed, GERALD FINDLAY, PROPRIETOR AND PROJECTIONIST. *The owner takes himself pretty seriously*, Jim thought as he went inside.

The area that passed for the theatre's lobby was shopworn beyond all safety standards. The concession stand hadn't seen a fresh nutty bar for a good many years. Spiderwebs hung inside the popcorn popper.

"Hello?" Jim called.

A small door, flanked by tattered red velvet drapes lay straight ahead. Jim looked inside. Wooden chairs were strewn about, mostly facing in the general direction of a small movie screen.

Rain beat down noisily on the building's metal frame. A cloying dampness thickened the air. *What a dump. How could anyone sit in here for even a five-minute cartoon, let alone an entire movie?* he wondered.

Jim shook his head in defeat. *Forget this whole thing of holding the camping spot. He would drive back to the city right now.* He turned around, kicking at the filthy, rippled old carpeting. As he did, the familiar click-whir of a projector penetrated the stale air. Seconds later, the screen in front of him lit up and letters shimmered across the screen: Gerald Findlay, Proprietor and Projectionist.

Way too much self-promotion, Jim thought. *I have to get out of here.*

The letters faded to white, replaced by an image of the theatre, complete with the jerry-rigged marquee.

That's not a photograph, Jim realized. *That's an old film reel of Main Street, a really old film, judging by the cars driving by. Man, cars were huge back then. Ridiculous. People looked so funny, too. The women with their bouffant hair and the men with their droopy moustaches.*

He stared transfixed by the celluloid memories scrolling across the screen, folks going about the ordinary lives they lived—at least fifty years ago. He rubbed his hand against his face and blinked several times. Were his eyes playing tricks on him? The scene before him broadened and revolved as if the cameraman had pulled back and was slowly turning on the spot.

A tsunami of vertigo crashed against Jim. He grabbed the back of a chair and fought with all his might to stay upright.

Whoa, wait! How can that be? There's that same kid standing by the drugstore.

Jim's stomach heaved. *Run*, he told himself, but his body held him fast in place, staring at the movie screen.

The screen flickered twice and went black. Jim choked. Clouds of greasy black smoke rolled toward him. Flames exploded through Gerald Findlay, Proprietor and Projectionist's glass doors.

The theatre's on fire. No, no—it's a film of a fire!

Jim lurched toward the exit, stumbling heavily against a wooden chair. Panic blocked the pain. Gasping for air, he crossed the lobby, pushed open the glass doors, and lunged out to the sidewalk. Concrete under his feet had never felt as good. He leaned against a lamppost long enough to calm his breathing.

The sun was out. Regular-looking people had appeared, lazily strolling from store to store. Traffic flowed normally. Cars were parked at the curbs. *His car! Where was his car? There it was, right where he had left it in front of the drugstore. Okay then, where was the weird little kid he had talked to? The same one he'd seen on the screen? Gone, that's where the little kid was. Absolutely gone, vanished, simply not there anymore.*

Jim staggered to his car, opened the door, and let himself fall in. Beyond the windshield, everyday life played out around him. He closed his eyes, rubbed his face, and massaged his jaw until he felt himself settle.

What had just happened?

Nothing. That's what had just happened. Obviously, he'd fallen asleep. He'd dreamed the whole thing. That explained everything—well, everything except for the blood dribbling from the gash on his knee where he'd tripped against that wooden chair in the deserted theatre. Jim drew in a deep breath.

Jim decided he would ask about Gerald Findlay, Proprietor and Projectionist, next time he was in town. He started his car and drove toward the highway. He was going back to the city to wait for his friends and would ride back up with one of them. He'd had enough time to himself to last him for a good long while.

Jim never told anyone about his strange encounter that day, but the next night, around a roaring campfire, he did tell his friends a fabulous new campfire story, about a guy camping alone in the rain getting so bored that he drove into the nearest town . . .

Well, you know the rest of that story.

HAPPY BIRTHDAY

Amanda opened her eyes a tiny bit. Happiness coursed through her body. She curled her toes around the soft flannel lining of her sleeping bag and smiled to herself in delight. What a great sleep she'd had! Nothing so refreshing as spending the night safe and sound, surrounded by loved ones, all hidden away in the deep, dark wood, where the world's troubles would never think to come looking.

Better still, today was her birthday. The only present Amanda had wanted was a family camping trip at the lake, and everyone—all her brothers and sisters, grandparents, and, of course, her parents—had made that happen for her. She couldn't remember ever feeling so content, but then she'd never celebrated her twentieth birthday before. Next month she'd be off to college, but for now she could just enjoy.

This evening, maybe while they were barbecuing dinner, she would say a few words to make sure everyone knew how very grateful she was that they had all come together to celebrate her day. Three generations, all of them healthy and happy and knowing that without one extraordinary date with destiny, a long time ago and far away, none of them would ever have even been born.

That place was London, England, and the date was Saturday, September 7, 1940. The Second World War was at its ugly and deadly worst. Nazi bombers roared across the English Channel day after day, destroying the city of London and killing thousands of innocent civilians.

Amanda's grandmother was just a baby then and the light of her mother's life. At the first sound of the air-raid sirens, the young mother would bundle her tiny daughter in a blanket and hurry to the nearby shelter. And that's where they would spend the day, huddled underground with hundreds of other Londoners as the enemy's planes swarmed overhead, pummelling the city with bombs.

As night fell, people returned to their homes. But on this night, that little baby and her mother were stopped at their front door. Holding the child in one arm, the woman pulled the house key from her pocket and fitted it into the lock. Suddenly a swirl of dark, dense air filled the doorway. She stepped back, grasping the baby more tightly. The whirling mass lengthened and thickened until she could make out the blurred image of a figure, a man with long, uncombed hair flowing down over a dirty white robe.

"Do...not...stay...here...at...night," the being ordered in an eerie whisper. "Return...to...the...shelter."

The air buzzed with static electricity for a moment, and then the phantom vanished.

Terrified, the young mother clutched her child and ran out into the street screaming for help. An elderly neighbour tried to reassure her, reminding her that the Germans never attacked at night. But she wouldn't be comforted. She insisted on going to the nearest shelter immediately and staying there overnight.

Hours later, Nazi bombers assaulted London with an attack that would prove to be the first of fifty-seven consecutive night raids on the city. Tens of thousands of people were killed, and entire areas of the city flattened. The doorframe where the apparition had manifested took a direct hit. If it hadn't been for that supernatural warning, Amanda's grandmother would have died as a tiny infant and the people gathered to celebrate Amanda's birthday would never have been born.

Yes, she had many people to be grateful to, some of whom she had never met and another being she would never fully comprehend.

With that thought, the birthday girl scrambled from her sleeping bag, thrust open the tent's flaps, and called out, "Good morning! Last one into the lake's a rotten egg!"

LIFESAVING LIGHT

Sarah and Tom had spent a fabulous day with friends at a lakeside cabin. They had all been having so much fun visiting that they hadn't paid attention to the time. It was only when they began to get chilly that they noticed the sun was setting.

"We'd better get going," Tom said.

"Stay here for the night," their hosts urged.

Tom looked over at Sarah. The campfire's embers were burning low enough that it was difficult for him to read the expression on her face, but he knew she always preferred sleeping in her own bed, or in this case, her own sleeping bag—they were holidaying at a campsite just across the lake. He also knew that right now, Sarah was still grieving from her grandmother's death, and he wanted her to be as comfortable as she possibly could be.

"Thanks, but we'll be fine," he assured their friends.

The couple said their goodbyes and walked down to the dock, where their boat was tied. As always, the reliable motor roared to life and soon Tom and Sarah were well on their way across the lake.

They were a good distance from shore when a nasty wind picked up, a wind strong enough to blow them a bit off course. If they had been making the trip in daylight, Tom wouldn't have been worried, but twilight had been gathering when they'd headed out. The wind was picking up. This needed to be a fast trip.

Churned by the wind's fury, the waves swelled and the boat began to take on water. Sarah and Tom were in trouble. Neither of them said a word; there was nothing to say. Besides, they couldn't have heard one another over the cacophony of sounds: the motor, the wind whipping against them, and the waves slapping the sides of the boat. Then, suddenly, one noise stopped. The motor had quit; it just sputtered and died. Without power, they would be completely at the mercy of the wind and waves. Tom tried desperately to restart the engine, but it was hopeless.

A brutal wave hit the bow, flooding the boat with knee-high water. They were sinking. The waves were enormous. It was only luck, really, that they hadn't capsized yet. Tom knew their time was running out. The couple could only cling to each other and pray. Tom could barely feel Sarah's body wrapped in his arms. They were both numb with cold and fear. At least they'd go down together—but what of the pain it would bring to their families? As it was, Sarah's family had just lost their beloved matriarch. So many people would be devastated, and Tom knew he could have prevented the tragedy by insisting that they accept their friends' hospitality for one night.

He opened his eyes and looked toward the sky, pleading with fate to spare them. As he did, a swirling mass of blue, pulsating light appeared just above the waves' crest ahead of them. It darted from left to right.

It's as if that light's beckoning us, he thought.

"Sarah!" he yelled, shaking his wife from her fright-induced trance. "Snap out of it! Look over there. Something's come to help us. We need to follow it."

Too dazed and frightened to question her husband's logic, Sarah grabbed for the paddles stored under the gunwales. The oars' thin blades felt woefully inadequate against the brute force of the windstorm, but it was all they could do. And now she saw it, too—the blue glow hovering just above the swells. It pulsated steadily as if waiting for them.

Tom's right, the light's trying to guide us, Sarah realized.

They dug their paddles into the angry black water and pulled with all their might, but soon their bodies were too drained and numb to take even one more stroke. The pulsing blue glow hovered.

By daybreak, the wind had calmed. Tom and Sarah roused themselves, relieved to realize they had survived the night. Tom looked skyward to thank whatever deity had protected them. The blue ball of light still floated nearby, as if watching them.

Tom rubbed his eyes. Could he believe what he was seeing? Land just ahead, right where the light was hovering. They had drifted into a shallow cove. With their last ounce of strength, the couple paddled to shore. When they looked up again, the light was gone.

They rested on the rocky shore, overwhelmed by their ordeal but very grateful to have survived. When they were able to, they walked to the nearest cabin and found the help they so badly needed.

Once they had recovered from their harrowing experience, Tom and Sarah tried to find out if anyone else had ever encountered a pulsing blue light on that lake. No one had.

Over the years, whenever they were asked about that nearly tragic night on the lake, Tom always credited the blue light for saving their lives.

"We don't know where it came from or why," he'd say. "All we know is that without that light guiding us, we wouldn't be here today. It protected us and led us to calmer waters. We would have capsized and drowned if we'd been in open water."

Sarah would always just smile, because she knew that her grandmother's favourite colour was blue.

TWO SPECIAL BLESSINGS

In the 1960s and '70s, most resort towns on the coast had dance halls, and those halls were always the place to be on Saturday nights because some of the biggest names in the Canadian music industry toured through that summer circuit.

One singer, a young woman, had an incredible story, one that's far too intriguing not to share. So as not to break her confidence, we'll call her Emma.

Emma was born in the slums of a large Canadian city to parents who were very good at making very bad decisions. Consequently, Emma's childhood wasn't great. "Disadvantaged" was the word people would have used to describe Emma and others in her situation, and disadvantaged she might have been. Except our girl Emma had two rare and precious advantages—blessings, really—and those blessings enabled her to rise well above her difficult beginnings.

Emma had a singing voice that sounded like liquid gold. She sang whenever she could and even occasionally when she really shouldn't have. Her second gift was that of intuition. She had it in spades. While she never went so far as to say she had ESP, that's exactly what most folks would have called it.

One day, when Emma was a teenager, she and a friend were sitting at a picnic bench in a park near their homes. The two girls were chatting amiably when Emma suddenly went silent. A second later, she stood up and started to walk away, calling over her shoulder to her friend, "I shouldn't be here. I have to go to the other side of the park right now."

Concerned, Emma's friend followed along after her, but when they got to the opposite sidewalk, there seemed to be no reason for her to be there. The girls looked up and down the street. Nothing seemed out of the ordinary. Even so, Emma was adamant.

"This is where I need to be," she declared.

After a time, a young woman just a bit older than the two girls hurried toward them. She was carrying a slip of paper that she held out to Emma.

"Please, can you help me find this address?" the stranger pleaded, her voice filled with urgency.

Emma and her friend looked at the paper.

"It's not far from here," Emma assured the distraught girl. "We're not busy. We'll walk you there."

The three young women walked along in silence. As they turned a corner, Emma pointed to a two-storey red-brick building and said, "That's the place."

"Come with me?" the stranger asked.

Emma and her friend exchanged glances and then nodded. Moments later they were standing in front of a glass door with the words SCHOOL FOR THE PERFORMING ARTS printed on it.

"Come with me?" the woman repeated.

The two girls followed the stranger into the building but immediately lost sight of her. She had been swallowed up by the crowd milling around a sign proclaiming that auditions were being held that day.

For the second time that afternoon, Emma was guided by an irresistible urge. This time her intuitive sense told her to stay right where she was in that throng of people and wait patiently for her turn to sing. She somehow knew that this day would be life changing.

Emma's friend stayed with her for a while, and the two kept looking for the girl who had led them there, but boredom drove Emma's friend away long before the crowd had thinned, and they never did see that young woman again.

Emma recalled, "I'd waited hours by the time I was next in line. I was hot and tired, but I put every ounce of energy into the song I sang, and that audition did change my life. The judges offered me a full scholarship for lessons at the school, and there it was, my ticket out of the slums." Emma worked hard to take advantage of the extraordinary opportunity, and she soon became one of the top stars in her genre of music. She continued to rely on her psychic sensitivity to guide her smoothly through the competitive music business, and along the way she shared her skills with those around her, even strangers.

One day, when she was shopping for a new outfit to wear on stage that night, a sales clerk looked at her and gleefully exclaimed, "You look just like that famous singer named Emma."

Emma was used to such comments but never wanted anyone

to make a fuss over her, so she always replied the same way: "I've been told that before."

As the clerk regained her composure, she moved closer to Emma, and that's when the singer's intuition struck again.

"Miss," Emma said quietly. "You need to see a doctor right away. Have him check your shoulder. You'll be sorry if you don't."

The clerk was taken aback, but she carried on with her job and found Emma the perfect gown for the evening's performance. When the delivery address turned out to be that of a nearby concert hall, the clerk knew for certain that this had been the famous singer, not just someone who looked like her.

Several weeks later, Emma received a thank-you note from the sales clerk. She had followed Emma's advice and gone to a medical clinic. The doctor had found a small tumour on her shoulder blade, but because she'd acted so quickly, the growth was easily removed. Any delay could have meant serious trouble.

And so, in addition to giving herself a wonderful life after a deprived start, Emma's intuition also saved that sales clerk from a serious, perhaps fatal, illness.

BARNSTORMING INTO ETERNITY

Matt was on his way to join his girlfriend, Shannon, and her family at their lakeside camping spot in northeastern Alberta, but on his way there he planned to stop and have his own private vacation for a few hours. He decided he would shoot a round of golf to calm his nerves. What a great and devious plan! He smiled contentedly as he drove. No one knew what time he'd left the city, so no one knew when to expect him at the campground. He switched the car's air conditioning to high and turned up the radio. He'd be on the links in no time.

Once he got to the golf course, he didn't have to wait long for the staff at the clubhouse to match him up with three other players. The trio didn't seem as anxious as Matt was to get out on the course, so he set about making hasty introductions and, hoping to speed them along, headed for the first tee. Unfortunately, there were already two groups waiting ahead of them—not a good sign. The course was crowded and their game would be slow.

The midday sun shone unrelentingly on the greens. Right from the first hole, Matt played poorly. Too late, he realized that part of the problem was simply that he was hungry. He should have stopped for lunch on his way out of town. As it was, he didn't even have a bottle of water with him. Sneaking in this game no longer seemed like a good idea, but it was too late for regrets now.

By the end of six holes, Matt was thirsty, hungry, way overheated, and losing his battle against the swarms of mosquitos. His heart sank when he checked his watch. He had expected to be driving to the campground by now. Shannon may not have been expecting him at a particular time, but he knew that the later he got there, the cooler his welcome would be.

He looked at his fellow golfers. They looked as miserable as he felt.

Why stay? Matt asked himself. *I'm outta here.*

He was taking off his glove and putting away his iron when a buzzing sound caught his attention. *Great, now I'm hearing things.* The noise came from overhead. He glanced skyward. Nothing but the huge hot sun and the wide blue sky. Looking up made Matt feel dizzy and slightly nauseated. He leaned forward and braced his hands on his knees. He didn't want to look like an idiot in front of these people he had never met before.

He tilted his head up slightly trying to see if they had noticed his distress. They hadn't. All three were concentrating on their game. Matt pulled at the sleeve of his T-shirt and wiped his sweating face. The buzzing was getting louder. *Was he going to faint?* A small dark shape appeared in the sky near the horizon. *Was he seeing things, too?* His stomach heaved.

Seconds later, the shape in the sky was close enough that Matt could see it was an airplane—but not just any airplane. It was an old Curtiss "Jenny."

How can that be? Those planes were trainers from the First World War.

The plane was close enough that Matt could even see the pilot with his leather helmet, goggles, and scarf—standard issue for pilots in those early days.

Matt knew he was losing it. He sucked in as much air as he could—hopefully enough to ward off a faint.

The vintage plane's angle changed, and the buzzing noise stopped. The classic biplane silently plunged nose-first toward the ground. Matt gasped and ran as fast as his shaky legs would carry him toward the place it was headed.

But when he got there, he could see nothing—just the pristine golf course with players dotted about it like toys.

Without a word to his fellow golfers, Matt staggered back to the clubhouse, dragging his golf bag behind him. He bought half a dozen bottles of water from the cooler in the cafeteria and headed to his car. He cranked the air conditioning to maximum and held one ice-cold water bottle to his neck as he drank from another. When he felt steady enough, he drove the car out of the parking lot and onto the road that would take him to the campsite. He hadn't thought he would be looking forward to seeing Shannon's family, but he certainly was now.

Once he found their camping spot, everyone, especially Shannon, greeted Matt warmly. Soon he was able to push his strange experience that afternoon out of his mind, but not before making a mental note to never let himself get that hungry, thirsty, and hot again. Clearly, that combination wasn't good for a body.

That evening, when the group was sitting around the campfire, Shannon's father came over to sit next to him.

"Have you ever played that golf course not far from here?"

"Not really," Matt answered truthfully, hoping his guilty conscience didn't show.

"We should do that one day, just the two of us. It'd be good. You know, in my grandfather's day, most of that land was a farm."

"Really," Matt said feigning interest.

"Yup. I remember him telling me about those days, the 1920s. 'Those were the days,' he always said. He loved the harvest fairs. They were big occasions then, folks taking time to celebrate the harvest and the fact that the Great War was finally over. Barnstormers, mostly ace pilots who'd made it through the war, would fly overhead in their Curtiss biplanes and then land on a nearby strip of farmland."

The man's rambling tale had Matt's attention now.

"Women just swooned for those pilots, apparently, and the kids were delighted. The men admired the display, too, but they tried to act blasé," the older man chuckled as he remembered his grandfather's stories. "They'd take spectators up for rides in their planes and do all sorts of tricks in the air. Real show-offs they were, but the folks loved them. The one that always got the crowd going was when they put the plane into a nosedive and then pulled out just at the last second before they crashed into the field."

"Really?" Matt asked, trying to keep his voice level.

"Must've been wild and crazy times, especially with prohibition being in effect. I've heard it said that the barnstormers had a lucrative sideline in smuggling booze to the thirsty crowds. It took some years, but finally the authorities prevailed and legislated flight regulations. Took all the fun out if it, my grandfather used to say."

Matt was grateful for the gathering twilight. He hoped no one would notice how the story had affected him.

"Too bad you never had a chance to meet that old man. You'd have liked him, Matt. He was quite the storyteller. He liked to say that the ghosts of those daredevils in their planes still haunt the farm fields."

Matt stared silently into the fire.

Shannon's father continued to reminisce. "That ghost story even made the newspaper here once. Not long after they'd finished carving the golf course out of the farmland, a bunch of duffers swore they'd seen a biplane do a loop-the-loop and then dive hard, nose first into the seventh hole. Trouble was, there was never any wreckage found."

Matt never forgot that day or that story. And he never went back to that golf course.

AND SO THE DAY BEGAN

Colleen Duncan pulled open the screen door and walked into the familiar old store. Generations of folks on holidays had counted on this place to keep a good stock of items that campers are likely to run out of or have simply forgotten to bring with them from the city. Colleen nodded to the well-pierced, thoroughly inked young man who stood behind the front counter.

Outside, children played hide-and-seek in a nearby grove of trees, and adults strolled along the path to the lake. In short, another day at the campground had begun—for everyone except Colleen, that is, because before her day began, she needed to get cream for her coffee.

She had only been awake for a few minutes, but she could already feel that this was a day she would need to start with a good strong mug of brew. She and her friends had stayed up way too late the night before, but it had been worth it. They'd had such great fun, all gathered around the campfire telling ghost stories.

Colleen walked to the oversized refrigerator in the store's middle aisle. And with that ordinary movement, the world around her suddenly shifted. The children's voices that had been drifting in from outside were suddenly muted, replaced by uncanny silence. Inside the store, all was utterly, eerily still, and there, standing right beside her, was a boy. He hadn't been there a second before.

"He was wearing a striped jersey and jeans that were way too short for him. His right hand was reaching up toward the top shelf. He seemed frozen in that position," she later recalled. "The air crackled like a lightning strike, and clouds of mist billowed by the floor."

Colleen looked toward the window to try and get her bearings, but that didn't help. Nothing out there was as it should have been. The trees were not the towering pines she had walked past only a few moments earlier. They were pine trees, all right, but only a few metres tall.

She looked out the opposite window toward the lake. The community dock wasn't there, only a rocky beach. She turned back to the statue-like boy standing near her.

"He was turned slightly away from me. I couldn't see his face. If he was aware of me, he certainly didn't give any indication. He was completely still, like he was frozen in time and space. That's when I noticed that he was ever so slightly transparent. His image was like onion-skin notepaper: I could see through him, but not clearly."

Colleen drew in a deep breath to steady her nerves as best she could. She watched in fascinated horror as the boy's image broke into shards and disintegrated.

Then the world around her began to return to normal.

"I could hear the children playing outside, running around the huge trees that grew near the store. Other kids were cannonballing off the dock and into the lake, and adults were milling about happily."

Colleen made her way back to the screen door. The clerk with his many piercings and tattoos called out to her, "You okay? Didja forget what you were supposed to get from the store?"

She shook her head. From that moment on, Colleen Duncan drank her coffee black.

A NASTY RING TO IT

Many people like to carry good-luck charms with them.
Seems like a harmless enough quirk, but have you ever stopped
to wonder if an ordinary item could really have extraordinary
powers? Some people believe that's so. Pyramid-shaped objects,
for instance, are thought to possess magical powers, and the
famous Hope Diamond is said to be cursed. Most folks, though,
think that any talk of curses or jinxes is just that—talk, and ridiculous talk at that.

Others, especially those who have owned a particular silver
ring, might think differently. Unfortunately, we can't ask any of
them. They've all been too traumatized to mention that ring ever
again.

No one knows exactly where this story begins or where it
ends. It's even possible that the story hasn't ended yet. One can
only hope that it has.

We'll pick up the tale of this jinxed piece of jewellery at a
pawnshop in a large western Canadian city on a hot day in July.
A musician named Steve was out for a walk. He wasn't usually
a person given to impulse buying, but this particular ring in the

pawnshop had really caught his eye. He was especially taken by the intricate engraving that circled the band. The delicate lines looked like a jumble of vines or some kind of fancy script. He'd never worn a ring before, but this one was something he suddenly just had to have.

Oddly, the woman at the shop seemed reluctant to take the ring out of the back corner where it nestled in the window display. She even tried to dampen Steve's interest in it by showing him other rings, but none of them appealed to the young man quite like that silver one did.

Finally, the shopkeeper nodded mutely and with deformed, arthritic fingers took the ring from its niche. Steve carefully counted out four crisp twenty-dollar bills, slid them toward her, and the deal was done.

Steve slipped the ring on the fourth finger of his right hand and walked from the store feeling entirely content with the purchase.

As he walked back to the rehearsal hall, Steve rubbed his thumb along the ring's gnarly surface and enjoyed the rough feel. Every now and then, he would hold his hand out a bit just to admire his new purchase. And every time he did, he felt more elated than the time before. *This*, he thought, *is the reverse of buyer's remorse.* Truly, everything about the ring appealed to him: the design, the shade of silver, how well it fit his finger—even the sales clerk's attempt to dissuade him from buying it appealed to Steve. He looked forward to showing it off to the other musicians in the group. Maybe he'd even have a little fun at their expense.

I'll tell them that the woman didn't want to sell me the ring because it's supposed to be cursed! That'll get the guys going. We could even use it as publicity for our gigs. People love supernatural stuff like that.

And, sure enough, just as he'd hoped, Steve's bandmates were intrigued with their drummer's unusual purchase and agreed the whole curse story would be a good come-on for the kinds of crowds they wanted to attract.

"Never know what'll work," Steve said to them. "The craziest things have influenced different bands' successes over the years."

And the ring may indeed have had an influence on the group's next performance. It was a show they had looked forward to for months. They were booked to open for a big-name singer playing at the dance hall in a nearby tourist town. What a great opportunity to get their music out to more potential fans!

The sound check had gone well, and everyone was pumped with anticipation for the evening's show, but incredibly, not long after taking the stage, the group was booed right back off again. Even the band members themselves had to admit it: they were terrible. Murphy's Law was working at its conniving best. Everything that could go wrong did go wrong. They started the first song out of sync and never did hit their stride despite Steve's persistent attempts to bring them all together with his drumbeats. They had been playing the opening chords of their third song with their mikes turned up to drown out the catcalls when the show's organizer signalled from the wings. His message was clear: off the stage now. Humiliation hung around the four like a large ugly cloak as they packed up their instruments and beat a hasty retreat.

The disgraced quartet threw their equipment into their van before the bass guitar player slammed the sliding door closed— on Steve's left hand, crushing his fingers well beyond repair. The guitarist was so mortified by the accident he had caused that he couldn't even go with the others to take Steve to the hospital. Instead, he walked off into the night, and none of the others ever saw or heard from him again.

The emergency-room doctors at the hospital sedated Steve so they could work on repairing his hand. As they did, an unscrupulous orderly named Paul slipped the unusual silver ring from Steve's other hand.

The doctors tried their best, but the Steve's left hand was never worth much after that, and his career as a drummer was over. If he ever noticed that his new ring had gone missing, he never mentioned it.

The thieving orderly hid the ring in his pocket until the end of the graveyard shift. Once he was on the bus heading home, he took a few moments to admire his new ring. He tried to put it on the fourth finger of his right hand, but it didn't fit. Maybe his mother had been right all those years, nagging him about his bad habit of cracking his knuckles. He tried the left hand instead. With some effort and a bit of spit he got the ring on. *Dumb thing looks like a wedding ring. Why'd I even bother to pinch it?* he wondered, suddenly angry.

The next morning the orderly was back at the hospital emergency room, but this time as a patient—a patient in a great deal of pain. The ring he'd stolen had become so tight that his finger had swollen hideously, and the ring had to be cut off. He was relieved to hear the heavy *clink* as the piece of jewellery landed on a sterile metal tray.

And that was where the cleaning staff found the ring.

"You want this?" a janitor said to his workmate.

"What for? It's of no use. It's cut right through."

"I'll get some solder. It'll be as good as new in no time," the janitor replied and tucked the damaged ring into his shirt pocket.

But the ring didn't stay in that pocket for very long. His skin under his shirt began to itch and burn. He just wanted to get home and have a long cool shower.

Forget the stupid thing, he thought, tossing the ring on the sidewalk in front of a pawnshop.

He was in such a hurry to get away from the ring that he didn't notice a woman scurry out of the store and scoop the ring up in her gnarled fist.

Who would its next victim be?

THE PIRATE AND THE BELLHOP

Back in the 1800s, pirates ruled the waves, and one of the most infamous pirates in history was a Frenchman named Jean Lafitte. Lafitte honed his pirating operation until it provided him a comfortable living. In death, however, Lafitte's conscience must have bothered him, because his spirit didn't rest in peace.

Details of Lafitte's life are as sketchy as his morals were, but we can presume that, like any pirate worthy of his eye patch, he left behind untold stashes of buried treasure when he died in 1823.

A hundred and fifty years later, at a hotel in downtown Chicago, two bellhops, Ted Serios and George Johannes, were on their lunch break. They were admiring a camera Johannes had just purchased. This new-fangled gadget, a Polaroid, developed the picture practically instantly. Serios picked up the camera, held it at arm's length, and looked into the lens. Much to the men's surprise, a grainy image showing the exterior of the hotel where they worked came out of the camera. It seemed that the camera had captured what was on Ted's mind.

Johannes, who was an amateur hypnotist, was curious about what had just happened, so he asked Serios for permission to hypnotize him. Serios agreed. He fell into a deep trance state almost immediately and within minutes began having an animated conversation. Soon it became clear that he was conversing with the spirit of the notorious and long-dead Jean Lafitte. The pirate confided that he had hidden a king's ransom in a particular spot in Florida.

Unfortunately, as lowly bellhops, neither Serios nor Johannes could afford to make the trip from Chicago to Florida, but word spread of Ted's odd ability to project his thoughts onto film and to commune with spirits. It wasn't long before fortune hunters stepped forward to finance the trip to Florida. Soon Serios, along with Johannes and their investors, headed south from the Windy City to Florida. Once again, Johannes quickly put Serios under hypnosis, but this time Lafitte's ghost refused to communicate.

The people who had financed the endeavour went back home, leaving Serios and Johannes stranded and penniless in Florida. The two became desperate.

"Maybe if the spectre won't talk to you, he'd at least let you take a picture of where he buried his treasure," Johannes suggested. He offered his camera to Serios, who peered into the camera's lens and then handed it back to Johannes. Much to the pair's surprise, the photographs were not of Florida at all but instead were grainy images of the hotel back home in Chicago where the two men worked and where they longed to be.

Fortunately for both men, a publisher named Curtis Fuller, who lived near Chicago, invited Ted to his home and gave him another instant-developing camera. As he had done before, Serios held the camera at arm's length and stared into the lens. The picture showed a building that appeared to be an airplane hangar. The image was clear enough that part of the word *Canadian* was visible. Investigation determined that the building was the RCMP airplane hangar in Rockcliffe, Ontario. Serios had never been to Canada. What could all of this mean?

Psychiatrist Dr. Jule Eisenbud of Denver, Colorado, a man with a special interest in extrasensory powers, became interested in Serios's ability. Eisenbud called a meeting with other medical professionals to demonstrate what he dubbed Serios's "thoughtographic" ability, but, alas, the former bellhop's mental and emotional state had deteriorated so badly that he no longer had credibility. He did, however, give the group a good show.

Ted took Eisenbud's Polaroid camera and stared into its lens. When the film was pulled from the camera, it showed a sharp, clear image of a double-decker bus. The experiment continued, and while gazing into the lens of Eisenbud's camera, Serios produced both colour and black-and-white photographs of buildings, cars, rockets, people, and animals.

Ted Serios appeared to have acquired this bizarre ability only after conversing with the ghost of a pirate, and, when questioned about his strange ability, poor bedraggled Ted would always refer to his first psychic experience under hypnosis and tell people, "Better ask Jean Lafitte."

Here is one more piece of this puzzle for you happy campers to think about. Tonight, after you douse your campfire and snuggle into your sleeping bags, keep in mind that this is a true story, documented fully in Dr. Eisenbud's book, *The World of Ted Serios* (which you can buy online).

A VOICE IN THE NIGHT

There is a wonderfully chilling old sea story written by William Hope Hodgson and published in *The Blue Book Magazine*'s 1907 edition. The yarn was titled "The Voice in the Night." The following retelling is offered to those who camp by the majestic Pacific Ocean, and in tribute to Hodgson and his enduring gift as a storyteller.

"It was a dark, starless night. We are becalmed in the Northern Pacific," the tale begins.

A lone sailor named George manned the tiller of a small fishing vessel while his three shipmates slept. The man was lost in his thoughts.

Suddenly, from the dark, damp silence surrounding him, George heard a voice call out, "Ahoy!"

Too startled to reply, George strained his eyes to see who had called, but it was impossible to see beyond a few metres. After a moment he comforted himself by deciding he must have imagined the voice.

But then, there it was again: "Ahoy!"

"Who are you?" the frightened fisherman demanded.

"Don't be afraid," came the reply.

"Show yourself."

"I would but for your safety."

An oar splashed in the water below, and George ran to waken his crewmate, a boy named Will.

"We need a lantern," he directed. "There's something strange out there."

Will shone a light over the side of the fishing boat. Again an oar splashed, and some vague form moved in the dense haze.

"Make yourself known," Will called out.

After a moment's silence, the voice moaned, "Please, you must put your light away."

George stashed the lantern and once again asked the man to come closer.

"How can we know you're not a raiding party if we can't see you?" George asked.

"I'm alone in the boat. My wife's on a small island nearby. We're both so hungry. Do you have provisions you could share?"

Will and George exchanged glances. They could not let a fellow seafarer starve. They filled a box with food and lowered it into the dark until they could hear the gentle swells float the box away. Moments later they heard muted sounds of oars receding into the distance, leaving the two fishermen to settle themselves into uneasy contemplation and finally, fitful napping.

A few hours later, the sounds of oars splashing in the water roused them.

"Ahoy," the familiar voice called again. "I've only come to thank you. My wife and I are stronger thanks to your generosity."

"You're welcome, of course, sir," Will answered into the impenetrable darkness. "Let us take you and your wife aboard. You'll be safe. We'll take you ashore when this dismal weather lifts."

"Kind sirs, let me explain..."

Then the disembodied voice began to tell its horrifying story.

"We were aboard a ship bound for San Francisco..."

Will interjected, "I've heard talk about that ship! She left from Newcastle some six months ago. Nothing's been heard of her or any aboard since."

"Until now, I suppose," the muffled voice replied. "The ship was caught in a sudden storm. My wife and I were in our cabin below, and in the chaos, we were left behind when the others were swept overboard. Somehow, we weathered the storm and when the waters calmed, we built a raft and floated at the current's whim for days.

"Eventually, we drifted into a lagoon alongside a large sailing ship. The fog hung heavily, but even so, we were overjoyed at the prospect of being saved.

"I called out, but there was no reply. A rope dangled near the ship's stern, so I hoisted myself up to the deck. There was nothing living aboard save a hideous green fungus that oozed over every square inch of the boat.

"I shimmied back down the rope and told my wife there was no hope, that the vessel had been long deserted, but her hopes wouldn't be dashed. She insisted on inspecting the situation with me. I was sure that once she saw the state of the hulk she'd flee, but quite the contrary, she thought we could clean the vessel and call it our home until we were finally rescued. There were provisions in the galley and a small tank of fresh water.

"We set to scrubbing the ghastly lichen off the decks, and after a while had the place quite trim. For a few days we were happily hopeful."

A sob choked off the man's next words. George and Will waited respectfully for him to continue.

"We noticed that the mossy fungus had regrown in the places we'd cleaned, but now it was thicker. We'd run out of water, and there was only a bit of sugar left in the larder. I knew our end was near, but my wife was still determined to make the best of it—although I couldn't fathom how. Then, early one morning, I saw her stooped over a patch of fungus. She was eating it.

"I insisted we leave the ship right away and we made ourselves a little camp on the land surrounding the lagoon. That afternoon I saw a strange shape moving in the distance. I took a few steps toward it before I realized this lumbering mass of green-grey lichen had a grotesquely human shape to it. Slowly it dawned on me that this must be one of the sailors who'd been aboard the abandoned ship.

"I rushed back to my wife, but it was too late. She greeted me by holding her right hand out to me. A small patch of the terrible fungus grew on her right thumb. My heart sank. I walked inland to be by myself and think. I knew then for certain that there wouldn't be a rescue. It was only a matter of time before I, too, would show signs of the fungus on my body, and soon after that both of us would become blobs of fungus in deformed human shapes.

"And that is exactly what has happened. We will undoubtedly die soon, but we were so hungry, and your kindness eased our anguish. You must understand now why I can't come closer. My appearance is repulsive, and, of course, I cannot risk contaminating you and your boat, too."

Silence hung in the fog-heavy air between the two vessels for a while, and then the man in the dinghy spoke again.

"Now I must bid you kind gentlemen adieu."

With that, Will and George heard the familiar sound of the oars rowing away.

The voice in the night called out, "Bless you and goodbye." His voice was never heard again.

When the sun began to burn through the fog, Will and George and the others aboard the fishing boat prepared to be on their way, but before that, the two men stared into the distance for a time. They could just make out the image of a small rowboat receding in the distance. At the oars was a greenish-grey mass of fungus in roughly the shape of a man.

OGOPOGO: A PALINDROME
OF A MONSTER

Ogopogo, the monster long said to live in British Columbia's Okanagan Lake, has had quite an image makeover in the past seventy-five or so years.

Dating as far back as pre-European settlement, Native legends described the monster living in the lake as having a body as thick as a tree trunk with a head like that of a horse. Indigenous people who camped near the creature's domain feared and respected the beast. If they had not seen one of his feeding frenzies first-hand, then they almost certainly knew someone who had, and no one ever forgot stories of a monster rising to the surface of the lake and lashing its powerful tail.

After Europeans arrived and began to farm the area, they often found it convenient to swim their horses across the narrow lake. They always started that journey the same way, by throwing a dead pig or sheep out into the water ahead of them in order to distract Ogopogo while they made the crossing. Back in the 1860s, a farmer named John McDougal was one who made that trip frequently. He would tether two horses in a line behind his canoe and then paddle to the opposite shore.

One fateful day, however, he realized when he was a considerable distance across the lake that he had forgotten to offer the sacrificial carcass. For a moment he thought of going back to the shore to get an animal's body, but then he realized his horses would be exhausted before they completed the extended trip. McDougal decided that he had no choice but to press on. Seconds later, the lake monster's head cut through the surface of the water and one horse disappeared as if swallowed by the waves. McDougal grabbed the tie rope and pulled it taut, hoping to save the remaining horse. His efforts were in vain. The monster's head reared up again, and the second horse was pulled down, nearly overturning McDougal's canoe. Terrified, he grabbed a knife he had stored under the gunwales and cut the rope that had tied the horses to his canoe. Then, with every bit of strength he could muster, he paddled to the nearest shore. He lived to tell the tale, barely.

But that was then. Who would believe such a story these days? The whole incident might never have happened. After all, who other than McDougal had been there to confirm the details?

A much more recent sighting of the beast, this one carefully recorded, suggests there may indeed be some truth in the tales of Ogopogo.

In July 1959, Dick Miller, a newspaper publisher, was on a cruise around Okanagan Lake with several of his friends. They were enjoying the tranquility and gorgeous scenery when the surface of the water not far from their boat began to roil and froth. Miller grabbed a pair of binoculars and quickly focused them on the area of churning water when a monstrous head broke the surface of the lake.

"It was like an oversized horse's head. About eight feet long by seven feet wide," he reported.

Miller and his friends kept their boat a safe distance away and watched in amazement. They estimated that the creature was sixty to ninety feet (eighteen to twenty-eight metres) long. When it swam, they said, the length of its body bunched into five humps the size of small hillocks. Moments later, Ogopogo dove headfirst below the surface. They never saw him again.

Maybe the beast lost interest in the boaters and swam to the underwater cave near Squally Point that is thought to be the monster's lair.

But, not to worry, even if you're camping right nearby: in the last few decades, the tourism industry has remade Ogopogo from the killer beast he was into an adorably cute and appealing cartoon-like character who looks as though he wouldn't hurt a fly. You can try an Ogopogo-sized ice cream cone, or a glass of Ogopogo's Lair Pinot Gris, or take advantage of the photo op offered by the monster's huge statue in Kelowna's Kerry Park. Even his name is fun to spell: backward or forward, it's all the same to this lake monster, because the word Ogopogo is a palindrome.

SASQUATCH

Nothing makes a family feel more secure than knowing they're camping at one of the safest campsites in the province—unless that campground is near Harrison Lake, BC, where a wild beast is said to live.

But surely no one believes there really is such a thing as a Sasquatch, a half-human monster living in the woods of "supernatural" British Columbia—especially not one who leaves a trail of enormous footprints and a gut-churning stench in the air. No, of course not. That's just an old legend, a myth.

Harrison Lake is a beautiful spot: crystal-clear blue lake surrounded by sandy beaches, majestic forests, mountains, valleys, and a gorgeous sky. This is a place where a city-weary soul can completely relax and contemplate life's greater mysteries, such as, if there really isn't such a thing as a Sasquatch, why did they name the park near Harrison Sasquatch Provincial Park?

There are more than a few spine-chilling, seriously convincing stories about the beast, like this one, related by a highly esteemed author in his book *The Wilderness Hunter*. Before recounting the tale, he assured his readers that he was not a man who was easily spooked. He even went so far as to declare that ghost stories he had heard while living on the frontier "were of a perfectly commonplace and conventional type." (Who knew there was such a thing as a "commonplace" or a "conventional" ghost?)

The story concerns a man named Bauman, who, with his partner, made their living by trapping beavers. They knew they could be encroaching on Sasquatch country, because the previous year they had heard a gruesome report of a trapper whose body was found torn to bits. The area where his remains were found was covered with gigantic human-like footprints. Nevertheless, Bauman and his partner trekked to a particularly isolated stream in a mountain pass near where the body had been found.

They set up camp in a small clearing surrounded by a dense forest and, once established in the spot, they set out to place their traps. When they returned to their lean-to, they found the place had been ransacked. From their experience in the wilderness, the men presumed the mess was the work of a bear, so they simply retidied their temporary home and began to cook dinner.

After they had enjoyed their meal, Bauman walked around the small area to make sure everything was secure before they turned in. Unfortunately, what he found did nothing to ease his mind. There were no bear tracks anywhere, but there were enormous, human-like footprints deeply imbedded in the soil. The sun was setting by then, so there was no time for them to find another camping spot for the night.

In the wee hours of the morning, Bauman suddenly snapped awake. Had he heard something? No. There was no noise, but there was a terrible stench in the air. The trapper knew what wild animals smelled like, so he grabbed his rifle and fired in the direction of a movement between the nearby trees. His shot must have missed its target, because seconds later the ground around him shook as something enormous retreated into the impenetrable blackness of the forest.

The next day, Bauman and his friend stayed close together as they made their way to and from their traplines. By evening they were exhausted, and when they returned to their camp, they once again found their belongings in total disarray. Considerably more disturbing than that were the tracks the intruder had left. The trappers followed a clear line of gigantic footprints leading away from their camp and toward a nearby brook. The marks were clear, "as plain as if on snow," the author explained before adding, "Whatever the thing was, it had walked off on two legs."

By now the trappers' composure had been seriously shaken. It was too dark to hike out from their campsite, so they built an enormous campfire, and through the night they took turns guarding the site. All through the night, each heard branches snapping and every now and again "a long, drawn-out moan."

Needless to say, by morning they were more than ready to make their way out of the bush. Bauman offered to collect their traps while his partner stayed behind to break camp. These were familiar chores for each of the men, but as Bauman made his way to the brook where the cages were tied, he found that one of them had been cut loose from the others. He looked downstream and saw the missing trap lying close to a beaver den. All of the traps were empty.

He hurried back to tell his partner what had happened. When he reached the campsite, Bauman found it all in order, with packs wrapped and neatly arranged. His partner had done a good job, but oddly, he himself was not there. Surely he would not have hiked out on his own? Bauman called to his friend but got no answer. He looked around. There, lying beside a fallen log, was his partner's still-warm body. The man's neck had been snapped and "there were four great fang marks in the throat."

Bauman was terrified to see that the now-familiar footprints of an enormous creature (who, judging by the footprints, walked on two legs) were all over the area. Bauman figured that his friend, after packing their gear, had sat down on the log to rest while he waited for Bauman to return. The thing must have ambushed him from behind.

As Bauman hiked out of the forest, he had the terrifying sensation that he was being watched, but eventually he did make it to safety and lived to tell all the gruesome details of his encounter with the giant "half-human, half-devil."

Who would have written such a wild story? The author's name will be familiar to you, I'm sure, because he was none other than Theodore Roosevelt, the twenty-sixth president of the United States.

Fortunately for campers at Sasquatch Provincial Park, these events took place in Idaho, so tonight when you hear trees splintering under enormously heavy footfalls, you should not be too concerned—even though there have been Sasquatch sightings in western Canada, too.

Sweet dreams!

THE CHEATER

Stewart could hardly wait for his vacation to begin. He'd packed his car on Thursday evening and planned to be on the highway right after quitting time on Friday. By Saturday afternoon, he would be sitting on the deck of a houseboat watching the world go by.

It was late Thursday night by the time Stew had all his gear stowed in the car, so he went straight to bed. He lay down, expecting to relax and fall asleep quickly, but he couldn't get comfortable. After tossing and turning for what seemed like ages, he sat up, and as he did, an inexplicable feeling of dread washed over him. He got out of bed and paced around the room for a while but that only made him more agitated. This was definitely not good. He needed to be well rested for his long drive after work the next day.

He went downstairs for a drink of water, but the eerie heaviness felt worse in the kitchen.

Fresh air, that's what he needed. He tightened the belt of his housecoat, opened the back door, and took a couple of deep breaths. Finally, some relief. Stewart slowly shook his head, thinking that this really proved how much he needed his holiday. Two weeks of nothing but fresh air at the lake. He'd be a new man by the time he came home again.

Smiling, he looked up at the clear night sky. The view would have been stellar if it hadn't been for that street light at the end of his yard. How he hated that thing. The pole attracted every dog in the neighbourhood, and the light itself shone directly into his bedroom window. When he'd called the town to complain, a woman had told him street lights were there for security. He had said goodbye to her quickly before he said something he would regret. Fat lot of good the street light had done when his neighbour's car had been vandalized.

Stew took one more deep breath before turning to go back into the house. He definitely did feel better now. Falling asleep shouldn't be any problem at all. Except, had something just moved out there, near the street light? He rubbed his eyes and peered through the darkness toward the puddle of light. Was there someone standing there? Yes, someone was standing there. It was an old woman wearing a long flowing dress. She was stooped over as if she were carrying something heavy.

Stewart tried to call out to the trespasser, but his voice froze in his throat. The woman stared at him with cold, hard eyes, the skin of her gaunt face pulled tight into an ugly grimace. Slowly she raised her left hand and beckoned him to come to her. Paralyzed with fear, all he could do was watch as the crone threw her head back. She gave a muted cackle, turned, and shuffled away. Stewart fell to the ground in a dead faint.

When he came to on the cold, wet grass, Stewart was sore and confused. He looked around. Why was he in his backyard?

Then he remembered. He must have been sleepwalking. He'd certainly been dreaming, because he remembered an awful dream about the vixen of death coming for him. Slowly, his legs shaking, he made his way back to the house and into his bedroom. He put an extra blanket on the bed and climbed back under the covers. It was hours before he fell asleep, and when his alarm clock rang the next morning, Stewart felt as bad as he could ever remember feeling.

At work, people gave him odd glances. He must have looked as bad as he felt. Early in the afternoon, his boss called him aside and suggested Stewart leave early. With a grateful nod, the exhausted man turned off his computer and headed out of the building. He would go to the first fast-food drive-through he came to and get the largest cup of coffee they offered—maybe two. That should perk him up enough to make the drive. By this evening, he'd be more than halfway to the lake. He could do this.

And he did. That night, Stewart checked in to a questionable motel and slept like the dead. The next morning, feeling completely refreshed and more anxious than ever to get to the lake, he made the last leg of his drive.

Steering the car into the tour company's long-term visitors' parking, Stewart felt energized. He could hardly wait to get on board the boat. The sun glinted off the lake like diamonds, and happy vacationers milled around. He grabbed his backpack and suitcase from the trunk and hurried down to the dock. There was already a lineup of people boarding. A teenaged girl, no doubt a representative of the tour company, was greeting each person and punching their boarding passes as they made their way on the boat. The line was moving quickly.

Stewart looked around full of anticipation for the days ahead, enjoying his picturesque surroundings. He was so lost in his thoughts that he didn't notice the teenaged girl had apparently been called away, and an older woman had taken her place. He was standing in front of the woman before he recognized her: her long flowing dress, her stooped posture, and her cold, hard eyes staring at him. This was the same woman he had seen lurking under the street light near his house!

She leaned toward him to rip his boarding pass. Terror filled Stewart's gut. He tried to flee but only made it as far as the grassy mound near the parking lot before his legs gave out. As he watched the houseboat drift slowly out toward the middle of the lake, a shudder snaked up his spine. Had he just cheated death? That's certainly how it felt. He sat, leaning against his backpack trying to gather his wits and wondering what was happening to him. The houseboat was still in sight. He should have been on it. What to do? What to do?

Suddenly a flurry of activity out on the water and on the dock distracted his thoughts. Something was happening on that boat. People were streaming out of the cabins and onto the deck. Moments later, a trio of small motorboats sped from the dock to the houseboat. Stewart scrambled to his feet and watched the drama unfold. Soon it was clear that there had been a fire aboard the houseboat, but equally clear was that the potentially deadly blaze was being contained.

When the men who had set out in the rescue boats returned to the dock, Stewart overheard them talking.

"It was the strangest thing—lucky, too. The fire was in the only unoccupied cabin," one man said.

"But none of the cabins should have been empty. All the passengers were accounted for when they boarded," his colleague countered.

The girl who had been greeting the passengers as they boarded approached the two men. "Who was that awful old woman who barged in front of me just as the last guy was getting on board?" she asked them.

"Old woman? I didn't see an old woman, did you?"

The other man shook his head.

But Stewart knew exactly who the girl was talking about. He knew, too, why that one cabin was empty. He also knew that indeed, he had just cheated death.

THE HEADLESS GHOST

One of the oldest ghost stories in western Canada is also one of the most gruesome.

An old prospector, bitter and twisted from many years of searching and just as many years of failure, finally struck the motherlode. The gold was his! All his! The old man was well-provisioned and stayed by his claim for weeks while he figured out how best to protect his newfound wealth. He certainly didn't want anyone else to find out about it, so he decided he would just homestead right there by the vein of gold and bring out small amounts of ore every once in a while so no one would suspect the bonanza he'd discovered.

The man's plan worked well enough for a time, but the isolation began to warp his mind even more. He began to question if he had really found riches at all, considering that his cache had forced him to into the life of a hermit.

Hoping to counter the loneliness, the old prospector began venturing farther and farther away from the rudimentary camp-site he had set up for himself. These little jaunts of his certainly seemed secure enough because his location was so remote that he never saw another human being. Unfortunately, this also meant he still didn't have any human interaction, until, that is, he noticed a stranger fording a nearby river and coming his way.

Terrified that he might lose his cherished cache, the prospector took careful aim with his hunting rifle and shot the intruder cleanly through the heart. The man was dead before he hit the ground.

Now the prospector had an even more serious problem. What if the dead man's friends came searching for their companion and then started looking into other matters in these parts that were none of anyone else's business?

The prospector couldn't risk forfeiting his stash. What should he do? The dead man's body was too heavy for him to move and hide in the underbrush, so perhaps he could just cut off the head and throw it away. Then no one would recognize the remains.

And that is what the prospector did. He threw the intruder's head as far into the bushes as he possibly could.

Neither the murder nor the dismemberment did anything positive for the prospector's mental health, although for a few days, all was quiet. Then, as the nearly mad man had feared, friends of the deceased came looking for him. Despite the head being missing, they recognized his headless body by his clothes and carried the remains into town for a proper burial.

But not surprisingly, the dead man did not rest in peace for, it's said, when the conditions are just right, a headless ghost wanders the area, searching, no doubt, for his head.

And what of the mad, wealthy prospector turned murderer? They say his body was found the following spring lying in his lean-to. And the gold? There wasn't any, never was. That prospector, like many others, had lost his sanity a good many years before to that most fatal and incurable disease, gold fever. Hopefully, his soul is resting in peace—a headless ghost is enough of an ethereal population for any area.

BETWEEN THE COVERS

Shannon smiled as she watched the van pull into the driveway.
She'd been so looking forward to having her nephew Keith
and his family stay for the weekend. Those boys of his could
run around the acreage as hard and fast as they pleased and
still not get into any trouble. He could spend the nights with
the kids outside in the big tent and Shannon would invite
Merrilee, Keith's new wife, to stay with her in the cottage.
That young woman hadn't exactly had an easy time of it, mar-
rying into the family, but Shannon knew she could offer some
special comfort.

By evening, everyone was gathered around the campfire
happily singing verse after verse of every song any of them knew,
as well as a few they barely knew very well at all. Finally, it was
time to drown the dying embers and hit the bedrolls. They all
wanted to be well rested for a full day of fun tomorrow.

As Keith corralled his sons, Shannon drew Merrilee aside.

"The boys are fine out in the tent. Let's you and me bunk
together in the cabin. There's a lovely little bedroom at the back
that I'm sure you'll enjoy."

Merrilee tried to protest, but when she saw Keith nodding at his aunt's suggestion she gratefully accepted the invitation. Inside the rough-hewn cabin, Shannon showed the young woman to her room.

"I do appreciate this," Merrilee said. "Thank you. The boys are great fun and Keith's wonderful with them, but they do get rambunctious."

"You're very welcome. I'm just so glad you could come and visit," Shannon said, giving Merrilee a hug. "There's a book of short stories on the night table in case you would like to read a bit before you drift off to sleep."

Merrilee returned her hostess's hug and smiled as she prepared for bed. She lay down and was drifting off to sleep when it occurred to her that it would be polite to at least start one of the stories in the book Shannon had so thoughtfully set out for her.

She sat up, switched on the bedside lamp, and opened the old, hardbound volume. As she did, a small gauzy fragment of material fluttered from between the pages. Merrilee looked in surprise: it was a feather. It must have been caught between the pages. The feather, or piece of fluff or whatever it was, was so light that the air movement seemed to make it fly. She watched it dance to the foot of the bed and wondered vaguely how long the thing might have been tucked into the book.

Whimsy appealed to Merrilee's nature, and if she held her head at an angle and squinted her eyes just a bit, she could convince herself that the feather was moving on its own. If she squeezed her eyes nearly closed, the thing didn't look like a feather anymore but a pale image, a loosely woven likeness of a woman. Merrilee's eyelids flew open. She gasped. A miniature opaque figure of an elderly woman with snow-white hair hovered just above the bed.

Except, of course, that couldn't be.

Then the shimmering being smiled at her, and soft warmth cascaded over Merrilee. The vision was speaking, but her words seemed to be blown away as they came from her mouth. Leaning toward the presence, Merrilee heard her whisper, "All is well. You are welcome here."

With that, the illusion faded from sight and Merrilee fell into a deep, restful sleep.

The next thing she knew, the sun shining into the bedroom window and distant sounds of children playing in the lake had wakened her. Merrilee realized she must have overslept. She quickly pulled on a pair of shorts and a T-shirt and opened her bedroom door. Shannon was standing nearby holding a mug of steaming coffee in her hand that she extended to the sleepy young woman.

"Good morning," Merrilee offered shyly.

"I'm guessing you met our resident wraith."

The younger woman nodded.

Shannon smiled and said, "I'm glad you did. She's quite something, isn't she? Welcome to the family, dear. We're so happy to have you be a part of us."

Merrilee smiled back, knowing deep in her soul that something very special had happened to her.

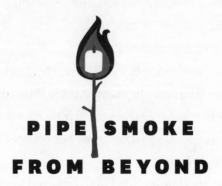

PIPE SMOKE
FROM BEYOND

Clayton looked over at his wife as he was clearing the last of the dinner plates from the table. That's when he realized stalling was ridiculous. There is never a good time to have an awkward conversation, so he might as well just start talking.

"Pam," he said more loudly than he intended to. "I need to tell you something."

The young woman looked toward her husband.

"You know that Mom and Dad want us to move into Gran's house now that she's in the nursing home," he said at a more reasonable volume.

"It's the least we can do to help out while everything gets settled," Pam replied.

"I appreciate that you feel that way, but there is something you should know. Gran's house is haunted."

Pam laughed. "That's a good one, Clay. You expect me to believe that your family let that poor sweet little old lady live in a haunted house?"

"Well, yes, actually. The thing is, Gran wanted to live there. You see, the ghost is my grandfather. Well, my grandfather's ghost, or however you'd put it."

"Right," Pam said skeptically and let the matter drop.

When moving day dawned, they were both on edge. By evening, the truck was empty, the small house was filled with boxes, and the couple's edginess had graduated to full-out snapping at one another.

Finally, Pam stood still, looked around the room, and, nearly in tears, said, "Clayton, this whole thing's crazy. What were we thinking of? Have we just moved into a haunted house?"

"It's late," her haggard-looking husband said, deflecting her questions. "Let's get some sleep. Life will feel better in the morning."

And he was right. Life did feel better in the morning. Pam woke up refreshed and was unpacking boxes before breakfast. *Haunted*, she thought. *What a dumb family legend to have. This place is going to be great for us.*

Clayton was so relieved to notice his wife's improved mood that he didn't mention their rough patch the day before. After all, moving days are always stressful. Everything would be fine. They just needed to get settled in, especially as he had to work out of town the next week.

By Monday morning, the house was in better order. Pam stood at the kitchen window and waved goodbye to Clayton as he backed out of the driveway. *Everything will be fine*, she told herself, but the icy shiver that ran down her spine told her something entirely different.

I'm being childish. It's time to get ready for work.

She turned the radio on to an old rock station. The tunes would keep her mind occupied while she had a shower and searched for her hair dryer.

The shower felt good, but as she rummaged through the packing boxes stacked in the hall, the good feeling left, replaced by the decidedly uncomfortable sensation of being watched.

It's all my imagination. If Clayton hadn't told me that stupid family story of theirs about his grandfather's ghost, I'd be fine. She pulled her shoulders back and lifted her chin, determined to get on with the simple tasks at hand. She found the hair dryer and took it into the bedroom. Then she closed the bedroom door—perhaps a silly thing to do in an empty house, but . . .

A few minutes later, she emerged dressed and ready to meet the day.

That afternoon, Pam lingered at work. There was no point in rushing home. The place was too new to her to feel like home yet, and Clayton would not be phoning till evening. She might as well do a little shopping and grab take-out dinner at the mall. The idea of watching some trash TV and eating her junk-food meal was appealing.

Before she unlocked the front door, Pam took a minute to steady herself, clear her head, and make sure she went into her new home with a positive attitude. She walked inside, took a deep breath—and started to choke! The air in the house was thick with the smell of pipe smoke. She dropped the bag of food and ran back outside into the fresh air.

Okay, this is way too weird. I'll go back in there and wait for Clayton to call because I'm telling him right then that I absolutely can't do this. We have to move out. Right away.

Pam calmed herself enough to go back through the door. For a moment, she breathed shallowly through her mouth. The air seemed to be fine. She tried a deeper breath through her nose. The house smelled lovely and fresh.

Maybe it was her—maybe she was losing it a bit from all the stress of moving. She wouldn't say anything to Clay till he was back home and they could talk properly, face to face.

That night, Pam went to bed early, intending to spend an hour or so sitting up in bed reading a book she had been trying to get to. She left the bedroom door ajar and settled in—until a small movement caught her eye. Had the door opened just a bit farther? No, it couldn't have.

Get a grip here, girl, she told herself firmly.

Then the bedroom door creaked open a bit more. Pam grabbed at the blankets in a vain attempt to protect herself. She squeezed her eyes shut, and as she did, a breeze of soft, warm air wafted across her face. Slowly she opened her eyes. The fear and tension she'd felt seemed to wash away. She felt entirely safe and secure. She sat up straighter in bed and looked around the room. Then she spoke out loud.

"This house really is haunted," she began, "and you're the ghost. You're Gran's husband. I've seen your wedding pictures. You and your bride looked happy and in love. You were so young when you died. What a tragedy. You must be wondering where your wife is and who I am."

As Pam spoke, she felt the spirit's comforting presence

surround her and she knew all would be well, that she might even learn to enjoy living in this very special house. She turned off the lamp on the bedside table and fluffed her pillow before happily laying her head down for the night.

The next morning, Pam awoke well rested and even anxious to get to know her ethereal roommate a little better. But the moment she stood up to put her slippers on, Pam knew. The ghost was gone. The house felt empty. It was no longer haunted.

Moments later the phone rang. It was Clayton. His mother had just called him to let him know that Gran had passed away.

"Mom said it was an easy death. Gran was actually smiling as she died."

"How's your mom taking it?" Pam asked.

"She's pretty good, I think. She'll make all the arrangements this afternoon, but first she was going straight home to change her clothes. She said it seemed like she smelled of pipe smoke. Funny, eh?"

"Okay," was all Pam said. These were Clayton's relatives. Sharing her experience wouldn't be helpful, especially not at a time like this. And besides, she didn't want to tarnish her own small encounter with life on the other side of the veil.

THE VANISHING POINT

If there's anything better than an old-fashioned sea story, then it has to be a yarn about a sailor, because it seems that folks who are called to the sea are just a little bit different than most others.

Take Curly, for instance. He loved two things. He loved the sea and he loved heights. He'd spent his life on the waves and was just plain fascinated by high places. And those two interests combined surprisingly well. For instance, if a rigging needed to be repaired, Curly was the man for the job. No mast was ever too tall for him to climb, and no matter where he was in the world, the moment his ship docked, he'd be looking for hills to climb and cliffs to peer over. In the evenings, when Curly and his mates gathered around the stove to tell each other lies, he would send shivers up the men's spines by pondering aloud what a marvellous feeling it would be to fall from a great height.

On a particular voyage, when his ship dropped anchor at a point of land near a west-coast port, Curly spotted an old, abandoned stone lighthouse. He was beside himself with anticipation. He could hardly wait to climb to the top of it. At first his shipmates tried to persuade him not to try, but when they realized their friend was not going to be talked out of his plan, they began taking wagers on whether or not he would succeed.

The sailors gathered at the base of the lighthouse. Curly was eager to get started, but now that money was involved, there needed to be a witness to the feat. It was nighttime, so they would not be able to see him reach the top. One brave sailor, an old salt known only as Ted, volunteered to follow the daredevil.

The two men entered the musty, damp tower and started up the crumbling stone stairway. When they reached the upper deck, they called down to the group below, but they were such a long way up that their voices didn't carry to the men. Finally, they decided to tie Ted's jackknife into his handkerchief and toss the bundle over the iron railing. Surely that would get the men's attention.

Just as Ted was getting ready to let the bundle go, Curly grabbed his hand and pulled it back. He undid the knot, added his own lucky coin, retied the handkerchief, and together they dropped their hastily devised attention getter.

They peered into the dark and listened, but they didn't hear it land. The bundle seemed to disappear into the night. Ted decided his word would have to be enough proof for his fellow sailors, and he turned to go back down the stairs. At first, Curly seemed to follow him, but then he hesitated.

"I know a quicker way!" he exclaimed and hurled himself over the railing.

Ted screamed a warning to the group below and fled down the stairs, terrified of the carnage he'd find at the bottom. He burst out of the lighthouse doorway, hoping that no one had been killed by Curly's leap. To his astonishment, his crewmates were sitting peacefully on the grass around the base of the tower. Nothing had hurtled down on them, they insisted—not the handkerchief bundle with Ted's jackknife and Curly's lucky coin, and not Curly himself.

The sailors searched the ground around the tower and on the rocky shore, but no one ever saw Curly again.

The next morning, not far from the tower, Ted found the knotted handkerchief containing the jackknife, but Curly's lucky coin was gone. Like Curly himself, it had vanished from existence.

THE REUNION'S EMBERS

A few years ago, Susan decided it was time to plan a family reunion. The get-together took a considerable amount of organizing, but the location for the event was never in question: Kinbrook Island Provincial Park in southern Alberta was everyone's favourite campground.

On a Friday evening, nearly a dozen households from the extended family had arrived at the site. The partiers ranged in age from a baby girl only eight months old to Great-uncle Fred, who had recently celebrated his eightieth birthday.

The family cooked a big communal dinner over a roaring campfire, with all the adults pitching in and the big kids helping with the littler ones. Afterward, they all sat around the fire chatting and kibitzing until the late summer sun was about to set. Babies and toddlers had long since fallen asleep in their parents' arms. No one wanted to be the first to leave the circle and break the magic that the gathering of loved ones seemed to create.

The bonfire was barely a glowing mound of embers by the time someone sensibly suggested that they had the rest of the weekend to enjoy one another's company and so they should tuck into their beds in various trailers, motorhomes, and tents in order to be well rested for a full day of fun tomorrow. Those nearest the fire's remains doused it with buckets of lake water and raked the ashes before turning in.

The weekend sped by. By Sunday evening, no one was ready to leave, but the realities of the workweek ahead meant they had to. Before breaking camp, though, they all agreed that these camping-trip reunions should be annual events. Susan couldn't have been more pleased with the way her one small idea had created such marvellous memories for the people she loved.

A few weeks later, Susan received a large padded envelope in the mail. She could see from the return address on the bulky parcel that Great-uncle Fred had sent it to her. Carefully slicing open the sticky seal, she pulled out a photograph. It was an enlargement of a picture, from the family reunion, of all of them gathered around the campfire that first fabulous evening. Fred must have stepped away from the circle to take the picture at twilight. He'd always been a creative man, and the shot was perfectly framed. Susan was tickled to have such a special memento from that wonderful weekend and quickly picked up the phone to call Fred to thank him.

"I'm glad you like it. Just a little reminder of that fabulous weekend you created for all of us," Great-uncle Fred said.

"I love that the picture's so dark and atmospheric. You'd swear it was taken with black-and-white film, except for the red of the campfire's smouldering cinders. I'm going to frame this and hang it in my kitchen."

And so she did.

Inevitably, summer's warmth gave way to fall, and then the long prairie winter set in. Susan found that glancing at the photo was enough to warm her heart. It was often the first thing she looked at in the morning and the last before she went to bed. She especially loved the way the family seemed to be drawn toward the campfire's last glowing embers.

Early one freezing Saturday morning in the middle of January, Susan made herself a cup of coffee before sitting down at the kitchen table to flip through the newspaper. From habit, she looked up at the photograph taken the previous summer.

The coffee mug fell from her hand.

The photograph had changed. The campfire embers were no longer glowing. They were dark, extinguished. She stared, unblinking. How could that be?

When her phone rang, Susan barely heard it. Her entire focus was fixed on the centre of the photograph, where the red glow had always been. It took several rings to divert her attention enough to realize she needed to answer the phone.

"Sue?" her mother's voice asked. "Bad news, I'm afraid. Great-uncle Fred passed away last night."

The embers in that photograph never glowed again.

ENTWINED

Tony and Penny's family wanted to celebrate the couple's fiftieth wedding anniversary with a gala celebration, but their anniversary date was just before Christmas, so it was difficult to merge everyone's schedules at that busy time of year. Eventually, December 27 was chosen as the day for the party. Of all the people gathered, only Tony and Penny knew how very significant that date was.

On December 27, all those years ago, the couple was honeymooning in a tiny cabin near a small mountain town. That morning they were surprised to hear a knock at the cabin door. Whoever was there must have made a real effort to get to them, because the cabin was isolated and they were all but snowed in.

They opened the door to find a young man bundled in a parka with a fur-lined hood pulled up over his head and down so far that it almost covered his eyes. He was delivering a telegram. At first both Tony and Penny were afraid that something had happened to one of their loved ones, but the man in the parka assured them the message came from a business in a distant city.

It seemed that the company Tony worked for needed him to do a favour. A customer in a city not far from where the newlyweds were staying had a problem with a machine the company had sold them. The fastest way to fix the problem was for Tony to take the train to the customer's plant and make the necessary repairs. In return for the inconvenience, Tony's boss offered to extend his vacation time by three days.

Tony was pleased to help. He could have the errand accomplished by the next evening, and the three-day extension of his holiday would give them more time in their secluded snowy hideaway.

As they finished dinner that night, the couple held hands across the table and made plans for Tony's trip. They decided that Penny would drive Tony to the railway station the next day. He would take the train from there to the city, and Penny would spend the day with friends in town. Then she would meet his returning train in the evening.

With the decision made, Penny rose to clear away the dinner dishes, but when she tried to stand up, she found that she couldn't pull her left hand away from Tony's left hand. Somehow, as they were holding hands, her wedding ring had become wedged under his.

At first they laughed about the situation, but then they realized they had a real problem that they needed to solve. If either one of them tried to move their hand, the rings cut painfully into their fingers. This required some thought. What could they do?

First they tried immersing their hands under cold water, but that didn't work. While they were still at the sink, they poured dish soap over their conjoined hands, but still the rings wouldn't unlock. Penny fetched her jar of cold cream and they slathered the oily goo over their hands. Nothing freed them. They sat back down at the table because that was the way their hands were most comfortable.

Finally Tony said, "I'm sorry, but I'm afraid we'll have to cut one of the rings," and with that he picked up the only file available to him—a small metal nail file.

He worked till nearly 2:00 a.m. before he finally managed to cut through the ring. The exhausted couple went to bed and slept soundly for many hours longer than they had planned to. By the time they woke up, it was too late for Tony to catch the train. But he had given his word that he would fix the customer's problem, so there was no choice: he'd have to drive.

"Come with me," he said to his bride. "We'll make a day of it."

"It'll be fun," Penny nodded.

The couple set out together and enjoyed the winter drive. While Tony was attending to the repair, Penny window-shopped. As they drove back to the cabin that evening, Penny told Tony that she thought their rings getting stuck together was a supernatural message intended to keep them together rather than apart for the day. Tony laughed and told her she was being silly.

It was late by the time got back, and they were tired from their long drive. They turned on the radio to listen to some relaxing music as they lay in bed. A news broadcast interrupted one of their favourite Frankie Valli songs. There had been a terrible accident. Snow had caused a train to slide off the tracks at a bend. Thirteen people were killed. It was the train Tony would have taken to get back to the cabin, but thanks to the freak circumstance of their rings getting entwined, they had slept in and Tony had not been aboard the doomed train.

And so, without knowing it, Tony and Penny's family planned the party for a date that was really just as special as their wedding day. The couple happily and uneventfully held hands through the whole celebration.

CRIMSON ROBES

On a beautiful summer's day, two friends, Philip and Frank, set out in their boat to explore the lake near the campsite where they were staying.

"This is going to be a memorable day," Frank said. "I can just tell."

The pair had been cruising across the water for a couple of hours when they decided to stop for lunch. Philip, who was at the wheel, steered the boat toward a small inlet. They could put down the anchor there, have a sandwich, and chat awhile without having to shout over the noise of the outboard motor.

Philip stood up and angled his body in order to drop the anchor over the side just as a swell hit the boat broadside. Fighting to keep his balance, he fell heavily against Frank, and the two young men lost their footing. Philip righted himself by grabbing the steering wheel, but Frank fell overboard. For a moment Philip panicked, watching Frank thrash about in the unfamiliar water, but mere seconds later, his concern turned to laughter as Frank stood up. The water, it seemed, was only waist deep.

Philip reached out to give his friend a hand back into the boat, but as he did, Frank disappeared down into a cloud of murky water. He must have been standing on a sandbar that had washed away under his weight.

Philip jumped in after his friend, but the water was so muddy that he couldn't see anything at all. He dove down into the murky depths searching frantically until he thought his lungs would burst. Finally, he had to push himself back up to the surface—without Frank.

Trying to compose himself enough to take another deep breath, Philip stayed at the surface, treading water. He was about to dive down again when a flash of something on the nearby beach caught his eye, something red, like a piece of red cloth. Impossible. He looked again. There was definitely nothing red on the beach, but there was something much, much better: his friend Frank. The young man was struggling out of the water and onto the shore. Moments later, the two were reunited.

"You all right?" Philip asked.

Frank nodded, still fighting for breath.

They sat in silence on the rocky beach, catching their breath.

"This wasn't the kind of memorable day we'd planned," Frank said, shaking his head. "I could easily have made the swim to shore, but the shock of the bottom dropping out from under me totally took my breath away."

"You went down like a rock," Philip agreed.

"I must've lost consciousness for at least a moment or so, because I have this dream-like memory of a man wearing a bright-red cloak. He lifted me up to the surface of the water."

"A red cloak? That's weird. I thought I saw something red fluttering on the beach," Philip recalled.

"Scared us both into seeing things, I guess. You know, if you don't mind I think I'd like to head back to our campsite."

Philip nodded.

Three hundred kilometres away, Frank's father had drifted off to sleep while watching a baseball game. Minutes later, he awoke suddenly and jumped to his feet.

"Whatever is the matter?" his wife asked.

"It's Frank. I've just had a terrible dream about Frank."

"Frank? He and Philip are camping this weekend."

His voice shaking, Frank's father told his wife, "I dreamed that a man wearing a long, crimson-coloured robe held Frank in his arms. He was carrying him out of deep water. Then he gently set Frank down on a rocky shore. The dream was so real. I could even see the man's cloak flowing and fluttering in the breeze."

Frank's mother dropped the plate of cookies she had been carrying. Her voice shook as she told her husband, "I think our boy may have been saved from drowning this afternoon. St. Stanislaus wears a crimson cloak, and he's the patron saint of drowning men."

First thing the next morning, Frank's parents went to a little shop near their house that they knew kept a good collection of odd icons and medallions. When Frank returned home the next day, his parents hugged him extra tightly. They weren't surprised at all to hear of his frightening misadventure.

Frank's mother handed him a small coin bearing the image of a man dressed in a long crimson robe.

"Please tell me you'll carry this with you every day for the rest of your life," his mother pleaded.

"Of course," the young man said quietly.

Frank kept his word to his mother and lived to a ripe old age.

HIS BROTHER'S DREAM

This old seafaring legend is usually purported to be a true story, and it might well be. It's certainly a thought-provoking tale, as puzzling today as when the events are said to have taken place, nearly two hundred years ago. It's no wonder it's still told around campfires in western Canada.

In the mid-1800s, Adrian Christian was a lad living with his parents and younger brother, Thomas, in a small cottage on the Isle of Man, off Britain's rugged east coast. Life was a struggle, but they were a close and loving family, so for the most part, the boys had a happy childhood.

Adrian, however, was occasionally plagued by a dreadful nightmare, one that was to haunt him most of his life. By the time he was in his teens, he had had the dream so often that his mother knew the terrible details and was troubled enough by the images her son described that she wrote out the particulars in the family bible as follows:

"Adrian dreams that he is the captain of a ship and his brother, Thomas, is on another ship that is sinking. Terrified, Adrian turns his ship around and heads into the storm to save him."

What a terrible vision for anyone to have in their head and in their heart.

In that era, tradition and necessity combined to dictate that most young men from the Isle of Man went on to become sailors, so it was no coincidence that when Adrian was old enough to be helpful aboard a ship, he began his career on the sea. Young Thomas followed in his older brother's footsteps.

Periodically over the years, whether he was working on a ship or at home on leave, Adrian's sleep would be disturbed by the horrors of that recurring dream from his childhood, of battling heavy seas to get to Thomas's foundering ship in time to save him. By the time he was a middle-aged man, he had lived through the nightmare dozens of times.

Adrian was a skillful sailor and rose through the ranks until he was captain of the powerful ship *British India*. One early September day, he was sailing from Sydney, Australia, to Burma (now Myanmar). It was a voyage Adrian had made many times throughout his career, and once the ship was safely on its course, he left the deck and went below for a nap.

He fell into a deep sleep the moment he put his head down. Seconds later he sat bolt upright in bed, drenched in a cold sweat. He had had the dream again, and this time the events felt even more real than ever before. Adrian was a brave man, but one thing he could never bear was the thought of losing his beloved brother. The dream echoed in his mind until he climbed out of his bunk to go up and join his men on the deck. He needed to distract himself from the anguish of the dream.

That night he was exhausted and uneasy, so he was grateful to fall asleep quickly. But he had no sooner drifted off than the dream began to play in his head again. This time, though, the terror was even worse because a glowing, transparent mirage of a being appeared and extended its hand toward Adrian. A single word, "Family," was scrawled upon the spectre's palm.

Adrian sat up in a panic, terrified that Thomas's life really was in jeopardy. As he checked his ship's charts, he was overcome with the conviction that he needed to change course immediately.

He turned to his crew and ordered, "Swing to and head the ship directly north."

The sailors were surprised by their usually calm captain's sudden change in demeanour. They were also afraid.

"Those are dangerous waters," the most senior of the men pointed out.

But the captain repeated his order. Soon the ship was plowing through the oil-black waters heading north. A thick fog rolled in, and the sailors had almost no visibility.

Suddenly, the ship's lookout cried out, "Ship dead ahead! She's sinking!"

They were close enough to hear the cries of fear aboard the endangered ship.

"Captain," the lookout cried out again, "She's going down fast."

"Heave to and get those poor souls aboard," Adrian ordered.

British India's crew worked tirelessly, their own lives in jeopardy, until finally all of the nearly three hundred souls aboard the sinking ship were safely aboard Captain Adrian Christian's sturdy vessel, including the captain of the destroyed ship, who was none other than Thomas Christian, Adrian's younger brother.

All those terrifying dreams that Adrian had endured throughout his life had been a premonition, preparing him for this lifesaving encounter.

As Thomas's foundering ship gave one final, ear-piercing crack, it broke apart. The bow lifted above the waves for a moment, just long enough for Adrian to read her name: *Family*.

THE DOCTOR'S HOUSE CALL

Doc was one of the most popular men in the small, west-coast town. He was a surgeon by specialty. He had taken out more tonsils and appendixes in his lifetime than most city doctors had ever seen.

One winter's evening, after a particularly hard day, Doc went to bed early. He was just drifting off to sleep when he heard his front doorbell ring. He grabbed the pillow and put it over his head, hoping that the caller would think he was out and would just go away.

But the bell rang again and again and again. Clearly, someone needed him. Cursing as he struggled out of his warm bed, he grabbed his robe and stumbled downstairs to see who was at the door on this awful evening.

Doc flung open the door. At first he didn't see anyone. Then he looked down and gasped. There on his doorstep was a small child, a little girl wearing only a thin coat to protect her from the snow and the harsh winter winds.

"Come in, child, come in," the surgeon insisted.

"No," the little girl responded firmly. "You must come with me. My mother's deathly ill. She needs a doctor."

"But I'm a surgeon, not a physician," the man replied, confused at this sudden strange intrusion.

"Please," the child begged.

"All right, then," he relented. "Let me get my coat."

"Follow me," the child insisted.

The child's tiny legs propelled her so fast that the man could barely keep up. Soon they were in front of a small house several streets from the doctor's home. Inside he found a desperately sick woman. He set about trying to bring down her fever and make her more comfortable. It was then that he recognized the woman. She had worked for him as a housekeeper the previous year.

With the doctor there to help her, the woman began to relax. Doc began talking to her, complimenting her on what a fine daughter she'd raised and how if it hadn't been for the child's brave trek to his house, she might well have died.

The woman lying on the bed looked dazed. She was so weak from the fever that she was barely able to speak, but she did manage to shake her head. Then, in a barely audible whisper, she told the doctor that her beloved daughter had died the month before.

"Her coat is right there," the bereaved mother said, pointing to a hook on the wall. "I keep it to keep part of her close to me."

The doctor could barely believe his eyes, for there was the coat the little girl who had come to his door had worn, except now it was warm and dry because it hadn't been worn for several weeks—at least on this side of the veil of time it hadn't.